A Maritime Fortress

A Maritime Fortress

The Collections of the Wynn Family at Belan Fort, *c.*1750–1950

MICHAEL K. STAMMERS

UNIVERSITY OF WALES PRESS • CARDIFF • 2001

British Library Cataloguing-in-Publication Data.
A catalogue record for this book is available from the British Library.

ISBN 0–7083–1671–9

Typeset at University of Wales Press
Printed in Great Britain by Cambrian Printers, Aberystwyth

In memory of Robert Charles Michael Vaughan Wynn, DSC,
seventh Baron Newborough,
1917–1998

Contents

Illustrations

Preface and Acknowledgements

The Wynn Collection consists of an assembly of boats, maritime and other objects from Belan Fort in the parish of Llanwnda in Caernarfonshire, north Wales. The Fort had been built and owned by the Wynn family of Glynllifon and Rug until its sale in 1986. The collection was the biggest single accession for the Merseyside Maritime Museum and in its variety filled many gaps in the existing collections. Its provenance has been enriched by the substantial Newborough Archive deposited at the Gwynedd Record Office, Caernarfon and the photographic survey conducted by the Royal Commission on Ancient and Historical Monuments of Wales in 1953. The catalogue consists of introductory chapters on the Wynn family, the circumstances of the acquisition and a history of the Fort, followed by eleven sections on separate areas of the collection. The number in brackets after an entry's title is the number of objects covered by the entry. The overall accession number is 1986.201 and individual item numbers are cited at the end and in the text where required. The archives held at Merseyside Maritime Museum are listed under D/WYN and these are cited within the text.

There are some overlaps; for example, some domestic equipment was used on particular boats. The napkin rings in the form of ship's blocks (1986.201.63, 1–3) from the steam yacht *Mira* are a case in point. Any object that can be linked to a specific vessel through surviving inventories or other sources is catalogued under that vessel's entry. There are many items where the link is not entirely clear, for example, the tinned food is certainly of a similar date to the *Vesta* but tinned food by that manufacturer is not found in the records. It is likely that, as the *Vesta* was regularly laid up at Belan, large numbers of portable items were taken ashore for storage and a proportion were left there after her sale in 1873. The same was probably true for her successors *Gwendoline*, *Pelican* (later *Sunbeam*) and *Ray*. Wherever it is possible, I have attributed such items to a specific vessel while leaving them in their generic section. The illustrations have been chosen to show the collection in its original context and its subsequent translation to Liverpool.

This catalogue would not have been possible without the help of the following organizations and people: the late Michael Wynn, DSC, seventh Baron Newborough, his wife Jennifer, Lady Newborough and Robert Wynn, his son, eighth Baron Newborough; Dennis Reeves of the Liverpool Scottish Museum, Liverpool; Clive Brookes of International Maritime Research;

Gareth Haulfryn Williams, head of Leisure Services for Gwynedd Council and the compiler of the catalogue of the Newborough collection of archives; the Gwynedd Record Office and Bryn Parry and Ann Rhydderch, the former and present heads and their ever helpful staff; Owain Roberts; the Commission for Ancient and Historical Monuments for Wales, Aberystwyth; Ron Davies Photography; Beken & Son, Cowes; Maldwyn Drummond of the Royal Yacht Squadron; Michael Connolly Photography; the Trustees of National Museums and Galleries on Merseyside; and the staff of Merseyside Maritime Museum, especially Kathy Davies, Tony Tibbles, Adrian Jarvis, Simon Jones, Dawn Littler, the conservators, notably John Kearon, Jim Forrester, Justin Garside-Taylor and David Letsche, the photographers David Flower and Clare Bates, and Lynda Rea who typed the manuscript.

All photographs are the copyright of the Trustees of National Museums and Galleries on Merseyside unless credited otherwise in their captions.

1 *The Wynn Family*

The Wynns were an ancient Welsh lineage from the Llŷn Peninsula. They acquired the Glynllifon estate, of which Belan Fort is part, in about 1700. John Glynne died without a son and his estate passed to his daughter Frances who married Thomas Wynn of Bodfean.[1] The conjunction of two substantial estates placed him among the most powerful of the gentry of north Wales. Local influence could be converted to a national role through election to Parliament which, in turn, provided opportunities for further political power and wealth. The 1688 Revolution had tipped the balance of power away from the Crown towards the landed interest and, on the death of Anne I in 1715, the Whigs supported the claims of George I; the Tories, including the Wynns' local rivals, backed the discredited Stuarts in the 1715 Rebellion. As a result the Whigs enjoyed a complete monopoly of power during the reigns of George I (1714–27) and George II (1727–60). The spoils of power were considerable because all official appointments including those in the army and navy were within the gift of the government. Many were sinecures with few duties and substantial salaries. The governing politicians, especially Sir Robert Walpole, maintained their hold on Parliament by careful use of patronage. Thomas Wynn was a staunch Whig who, through his local influence, could deliver the seats of the town of Caernarfon as well as Pwllheli and Nefyn.[2] He was member of Parliament from 1713 until his death in 1749; he was an equerry to the prince of Wales (later George II) from 1715 at £300 per annum and a clerk of the green cloth at an extra £1,000 yearly from 1724, and received a baronetcy in 1742. He also held the lesser local Crown offices of constable of Caernarfon Castle, forester of Snowdon, and steward of Bardsey.

Thomas, the first baronet, was succeeded by his son John, who was born in 1701. He was also an ardent seeker of office. Before his succession, he was appointed deputy treasurer of Chelsea Hospital at £800 per annum. He gave up this office to become an MP in 1754. From the Commons he campaigned for further rewards for his support of the Whig cause in north Wales against the Tory champion, Sir Watkin Williams Wynn of Wynnstay. He was never fully compensated for his lucrative Chelsea sinecure. He picked up a number of minor offices such as deputy cofferer of the king's household, surveyor general of His Majesty's mines in north Wales, custos rotulorum of Caernarfonshire and constable of Caernarfon Castle, as well as the auditorship of His Majesty's lands in north Wales for his son, Thomas.

Thomas Wynn, third baronet, succeeded to the title on the death of Sir John in 1773. He had been active in local and national politics since 1761 on his election to Parliament. He was not such a committed Whig as his father. It was not in his interest because the new King George III, who succeeded in 1760, was determined to reassert royal influence in Parliament and set out to build up his own party of 'King's Friends'. Sir Thomas as a 'King's Friend' was indeed rewarded for his support. He retained his auditorship and was appointed lord lieutenant of Caernarfonshire, as well as succeeding his father as constable of Caernarfon Castle and custos rotulorum for the county in 1773. In 1765 he made a good political marriage to Lady Katherine Perceval, daughter of the second earl of Egmont.

Thomas Wynn (1734–1807), first Lord Newborough (20).

On 22 September 1761, he founded at Glynllifon, the main family house, 'The Society or Garrison at Fort Williamsburg in Glynllifon Park' and the 'Holy Order of Sisterhood, United Connected with the Free, Firm and Friendly Garrison of Williamsburg'. According to its rules the Society and the Sisterhood were to meet annually on the anniversary of George III's coronation. This 'ostentatious gesture of loyalty' extended to the building of an earthwork fortification, Fort Williamsburg, named in honour of the Whig party's 'patron saint' William III. It was also a response to the older Jacobite (i.e. Tory) secret societies[3] and reflected a contemporary fashion for secret societies, though this was unusual in that it was not masonic or radical, included women and was in a rural setting.[4] The Society laid down an ambitious number of members including a commander-in-chief, a governor, lieutenant-governor, one hundred officers, twenty-four chaplains and an unlimited number of volunteers. A uniform of 'a true blue coat' with scarlet lapels, gilt buttons, buff waistcoat and breeches, and a hat trimmed with gold lace was required, and all members had to take 'a cup and cannon' oath not to divulge its proceedings to outsiders. The first elections to the Society on 22 September 1762 brought the membership to thirteen for the Garrison and seven for the Sisterhood – all relatives or immediate neighbours. It did not reach its ambitious complement and from the evidence of its surviving records, it lapsed in 1771. It was revived from 1791 to 1795 with Maria Stella, Lord Newborough's second wife, as patroness.[5]

Fort Williamsburg has been characterized as a folly – 'a rather pleasant unexceptional folly tower'. This does not seem to have been the case, because it cannot be compared with mock ruined castles designed as eye-catching features such as Rodborough Castle at Stroud, also built in 1761.[6]

*Maria Stella Petronilla
(1773–1842),
second wife of Thomas Wynn (20).*

However, Thomas Wynn and his sons had an enthusiasm for creating a fantastical landscape around Glynllifon. He (or possibly his successors) transformed the valley of the River Llifon with a lake, water features, a grotto, a 'druidical' stone circle and a hermitage. This landscaping project did not incorporate the fort. Although its outright military value for defending the county and town from a threat from the sea was debatable, it did have a military purpose beyond its ceremonial role for its society. Thomas Wynn as lord lieutenant was responsible for organizing the defence of the county, and this in turn depended on a part-time militia embodied in 1757 at the start of the Seven Years War.[7] Fort Williamsburg served as a rendezvous, training ground and armoury for this force.

Like many of his landed contemporaries, Thomas Wynn had an enthusiasm for building and reshaping the landscape.[8] Fort Williamsburg was a substantial project which survives on rising ground to the south-east of Glynllifon house. Its roughly rectangular plan measures some 400 feet surrounded by a ditch with bastions of different sizes at each corner, with additional earthworks to the north to protect the gatehouse. The centre of the fort was the parade ground which was overlooked by the armoury or 'summer pavilion', with a separate substantial barrack block behind it. No doubt the former was where the officers drank their loyal toasts every September, and later in the century it served as a military museum which displayed the standard of the Loyal Newborough Volunteer Association and flintlock and percussion cap muskets.[9] Some of these items may have been transferred to Belan Fort.

There is a watchtower on the north-west bastion which looks out towards the coast. According to the survey by the Royal Commission for Ancient Monuments, this tower may be a later feature. The photograph (D/WYN/7/8) of the fort in the collection, taken about 1850–5, shows that at that date it was much lower in height than it is today. It is likely that the Hon. Frederick Wynn had it rebuilt in the 1890s. He also built a watch house over the north gate of Belan Fort in that decade.

A warrant dated 28 September 1762 instructing Thomas Wynn to mobilize the militia and a list of 'the arms and stores in The Royal Carnarvonshire Grenadiers at Fort Williams Bourg and Carnarvon' of 31 October 1773 have survived, and these demonstrate Thomas Wynn's involvement and the use of the fort.[10]

Thomas Wynn became third baronet on the death of his father in 1773, and his political fortune seemed likely to continue, although his share of 'the

Glynllifon, the Wynn's main house, rebuilt after a fire in 1836 and later extended with the west wing by Frederick Wynn.

spoils of office' continued to be minor or honorary. He succeeded to his father's offices in north Wales and he was elevated to the Irish peerage as Baron Newborough in 1776 – a year which saw the creation of what Horace Walpole called 'a mob of nobility'.[11] In the previous year, he started on a second military installation at the entrance to the Menai Straits, Abermenai Barracks (later Belan Fort). His building enthusiasm and the upkeep of a substantial household including a house in London meant that he had to mortgage his estates. This was not an unusual predicament for a landed family at the time because most estates were held in trust.[12] The 'strict settlement' enshrined in common law from 1697 enabled a landowner to turn his heir into a tenant for life with the title held by trustees. This ensured continuity and stability of ownership.[13] Unfortunately, this financial problem coincided with a family quarrel and the loss of office and political influence.

The American War of Independence (1775–82) and the threat of a French invasion in 1789 had confronted the ruling ministry of Lord North with a major crisis. Thomas Wynn in later years claimed he had opposed the war and suffered 'a dissimission from such Appointments as no person was ever suffer'd to be deprived of by giving any vote in Parliament'.[14] He was defeated at the county election in 1780 and lost all his offices in the following two years. This could have been brought about by the political feud for control of Anglesey between the Pagets of Plas Newydd and the Bulkeleys of Baron Hill which spread across the Menai Straits to affect Caernarfon. This

Fort Williamsburg in about 1850–5. Note the watch tower with a semaphore signal on top of it and the telescope on a tripod to the left. The headquarters building and barracks lie behind the main rampart.

led to his losing control of the town constituency as well. He also had family problems as a result of his father's will which settled annuities on the children of his younger brother, Glynn, to the charge of his estate. These obligations do not seem to have been paid and in 1780 Glynn Wynn started a lawsuit at the Court of Chancery to enforce the terms of the will. The result, as with many other Chancery proceedings, was an interminable, complex, costly process, involving other family members, that continued until Lord Newborough's death in 1807 and resulted in the loss of one-third of the estates.[15]

To make matters worse, Thomas Wynn's wife died in 1782. He fled to Tuscany with his young son, John, and remained in exile for nine years. He attempted to preserve his influence in local politics through his land agent and was humiliated at the Caernarfon election in 1784 when his brother Glynn stood successfully against him. Tuscany in the late eighteenth century received many visitors from Britain. There were young nobles passing through as part of their 'Grand Tour', as well as longer-term and often penurious residents, including a government representative at Florence.[16] Thomas Wynn does not seem to have been a popular figure with his fellow expatriates and in 1786 his marriage to Maria Stella Petronilla Chiappini aged thirteen, daughter of the public constable at Montigliana, was a cause of local scandal and of more family trouble. There was an unsuccessful attempt to certify him as insane and to make his son a ward of court. The outbreak of the French Revolution in 1793 persuaded him to return to north

Wales. According to his second wife's reminiscences of 1830, the ill-matched couple, he fifty-six and she nineteen, were warmly received not only by their tenants but by all the notable local families.[17] Thomas Wynn patched up his differences with the now all-powerful Pagets and Bulkeleys who allowed him to sit as MP for Beaumaris from 1796 until his death in 1807. He also busied himself with local military affairs. The French again threatened invasion. In 1797 they landed a small expeditionary force at Fishguard which was repulsed. Nevertheless, the conquest of Britain remained Emperor Napoleon's prime strategic objective until 1805 when the battle of Trafalgar made this a complete impossibility.

Thomas Wynn's son and heir from his first marriage, John, died in 1800. Maria Stella bore him two sons in 1802 and 1803. The elder, Thomas John, inherited the title as a minor on the death of his father in 1807. He also inherited an estate that was heavily in debt. Retrenchment was the order of the day: the lease of the London house was given up and its contents sold.[18] It took some thirty years to clear all the accumulated debt that encumbered the estate.[19] In 1810, Thomas Wynn's widow married a Russian aristocrat and spent little time at Glynllifon, leaving her sons to be brought up by guardians. By 1818, they were being privately educated by a Mr John Salter of Whitchurch, Oxfordshire, who wrote to Coutts Trotter their guardian stating that he could 'no longer continue as tutor to Lord Newborough and his brother. I suggest Lord Newborough be sent at once to Christ Church (college) or else be enabled to see more of the world so he can conform with the habits of Society in general'. On 23 June 1820, Coutts Trotter received a bill for £9 for the two brothers cutting down fruit trees at their lodging at Whitchurch.[20]

Meanwhile, their mother, who by now was living in Paris, wrote many begging letters pleading for money. In 1821 on the death of her father, she seems to have discovered that there was something of a mystery about her birth. It was alleged that she was the daughter of a count de Joinville and that she been exchanged at birth for the Chiappinis' son. The count de Joinville was the assumed name of Louis Philippe, duke of Orleans, who eventually ascended the French throne. The count at the time of the birth needed an heir to ensure that his wife's wealth would pass to him and not revert to her family. She spent much time and energy trying to prove her claim until her death in 1843. Sir Ralph Payne-Gallwey, antiquarian, wildfowler, and friend of Frederick Wynn, supported her claim in his published research while a French contemporary, a Monsieur Vibruc, did not.[21]

The main house at Glynllifon was described in 1821 as 'much neglected and out of repair, owing to the minority of the proprietor'.[22] This was to change when the second Lord Newborough, Thomas John, entered his majority in 1823 and he began to build again. Abermenai Barracks was extended to become Fort St David's, later Belan Fort. A huge stone tower was begun in Glynllifon Park in 1826 which was to be a family mausoleum. By the year of his death in 1832, it was said to have cost £10,000 and was left unfinished. Between 1826 and 1832 he also sat as MP for the county – the last of the family to take a real part in national politics. In 1826 he attempted to get a bill through Parliament to allow him to enclose the commons at Llanwnda and Llandwrog and to eject quarrymen squatting on the commons at Rhostryfan. That he failed was due to the influence of other Welshmen in London. It was testimony to how much the political power of the family had been eroded.[23]

His successor, his brother Spencer Wynn, concentrated on his estate, country sports, his yachts and local county matters. The emerging political, religious and educational movements of the 1830s passed him by. The family was also relatively slow to exploit the slate deposits on its estates compared with some of the neighbouring families, especially the Assheton-Smiths of Faenol and the Pennants of Penrhyn. Slate was in great demand as a roofing material for the growing British urban and industrial centres and for export.[24] Nevertheless, over his long life Spencer Wynn succeeded in restoring the family fortunes and improving the estate. According to another redoubtable local entrepreneur, Sir Llewellyn Turner, he was 'a keen man of business' and 'an exceedingly good landlord and his farms were supplied with models of farm buildings'.[25] Indeed, he was fond of building: he continued the family mausoleum, constructed a massive wall around the park, probably added the dockyard to the fort, built a new church and almshouses for the village of Llandwrog and rebuilt the main house at Glynllifon. The latter burnt down in 1836. The rebuilding on a grander scale was finished in 1848. It is believed that Spencer Wynn designed the new house, which was in the Renaissance style with a grand portico leading into a spacious entrance hall.[26] A large stable block was added in 1849 and a modern estate yard followed shortly after. The latter included a gas works to light the main house and a steam engine to power a sawmill and other equipment. There were also huge kitchen gardens with greenhouses and heated walls for protecting delicate fruit trees. He also possessed 'the most opulent indulgence' – a sea-going-yacht.[27] He had sold the schooner *Sapphire* in 1838 and in 1847, at a time when expenditure on Glynllifon house was diminishing, he ordered a new iron-screw-propelled schooner, the *Vesta* – a bold and expensive indulgence indeed. While he lived at Glynllifon and had no part in national affairs, he was a conscientious local administrator. For example, he chaired the Quarter and Petty Sessions for the shire for most of his lifetime. He also expected to be consulted on local matters and was involved in local state occasions such as Queen Victoria's visit to Holyhead in 1859.[28] There were also regular trips to London for business and pleasure and many of the supplies and equipment for the houses and the yachts were purchased at the best London shops, as can be seen in the objects in the collection. By 1873, the estate encompassed 30,000 acres, which yielded a gross rental of £20,000 annually.[29]

On his death in 1888, the title passed to his grandson, the fourth Lord Newborough, William Charles, and the estates went to his younger son, Frederick, because his elder brother Thomas John (1840–78) had died ten years earlier. Frederick Wynn continued the family's building tradition and added a new wing to Glynllifon, which included a spectacular double-height billiard room. He also added a theatre at the back of the house, perhaps in imitation of his contemporary, the marquess of Anglesey, who converted the chapel into a theatre at Plas Newydd. Frederick also had a passion for boats and yachts. He also loved Belan Fort and he was responsible for preserving and adding to the collection of maritime antiquities that came to decorate its residence and boathouses. However, the expense of large new steam yachts was considerable and by the outbreak of the First World War, the estate like many others, was under financial strain. Frederick was ageing and a bachelor. He increasingly relied on his nephew, Robert Vaughan Wynn of Rug. Frederick wanted Robert to move to Glynllifon and give up Rug. This would have been difficult for his young family who found that meeting Uncle Fred, and his formidable housekeeper Ann, could sometimes be an ordeal. Frederick died in 1932 leaving a considerable sum to be paid in death duties. The estate was left to the Public Trustees with the income divided between his two nephews, Robert and, Thomas John, the fifth Lord Newborough (1878–1957), with Glynllifon for the use of the latter during his lifetime and Boduan (an older family house of 1736 rebuilt in the late nineteenth century on the Llŷn Peninsula and a favourite of Frederick's) and Belan Fort for Robert for his life.[30]

The fifth baron was the younger son of Thomas John Wynn (1840–78) who succeeded to the title in 1916 on the death of his older brother, William Charles (1873–1916). He made a career at sea. He joined the Royal Navy's training ship, HMS *Britannia* in 1895 as a midshipman and in 1896 was indentured as an apprentice to the Shaw, Savill & Albion Line on their barque *Akaroa*. After three years at sea in Shaw Savill's sailing ships, and a few months in steamers, he had sufficient time to pass his second mate's examination. He then travelled out to the Far East in the belief that there were well-paid jobs available on the inter-islands trades. After some initial difficulties, he secured a regular succession of jobs on Shell tankers and P & O vessels. He successfully gained both his first mate's and master's certificates. In 1915 he was commissioned as a temporary lieutenant in the Royal Naval Reserve. He commanded the requisitioned steam yacht *Vanessa II* from April 1917 until about May 1919.[31] Thomas John lived mainly in London and in 1948 Glynllifon was sold to the county council for use as an agricultural college.

Robert Vaughan Wynn became the sixth baron in 1957 on the death of his cousin. He continued his hard work to hold on to the Glynllifon and Rug estates. Many of the smaller farms were taken into direct management and others consolidated into larger, more viable units. This resulted in two directly managed estates with 2,400 acres at Rug and 1,000 at Glynllifon. Some properties were sold, including the house at Boduan and the island of Bardsey. He retained Belan Fort as a holiday home and a base for his yacht.

On his death in 1965 he was succeeded by his son, Robert Charles Michael Vaughan Wynn – known to everyone as Micky Wynn – the seventh baron, who had served in the regular army up to 1940, and then joined the Royal Naval Volunteer Reserve. He commanded a yacht which made no fewer than five trips to evacuate troops from Dunkirk. In March 1942, he took part in the raid on St Nazaire in command of *MTB 74*. His ship was sunk after he completed his mission and he was captured by the Germans after many hours in the water. He received the DSC for his courageous part in the raid which denied the use of the large dry dock to the German battleships. As a prisoner of war, he was an inveterate escaper and ended up in Colditz Castle. He was repatriated on medical grounds in 1945 and returned to serve with the army in the final land campaign. In his tank, flying the White Ensign, he helped to liberate the naval prisoner-of-war camp. After the war, he set up as a farmer on his own account, to learn all he could 'hands on' and he then assisted his father in the management of the two estates.

After becoming Lord Newborough, he in his turn was assisted by his son Robert, his heir, who took over part of the Glynllifon estate including Belan Fort in an effort to avoid further punitive death duties.[32] The fort, although a much loved family home, was another charge on the maintenance account. In the summer of 1977 it first opened to visitors. A ferry boat from Caernarfon, tea rooms, a pottery, a gift shop, a miniature steam railway, pleasure flights from the airport nearby and demonstrations of cannon firing, were all added attractions. Initially, it was a success and won a British Tourist Authority award in 1978. By 1980 it attracted 36,976 visitors, but by 1985 the total had declined to 16,525, which was below the break-even figure of 30,000. The fort had to be closed and was put up for sale in 1986.[33] Michael Wynn was concerned about the collection of boats and historic objects that had been part of Belan Fort and its dockyard for so long. There was some discussion about transferring the whole collection to the Maritime Museum at Victoria Dock, Caernarfon. It was not feasible for a small voluntary organization to take on such a huge project. In the end Michael Wynn contacted the Merseyside Maritime Museum to see if there was any interest in taking on the collection. After a survey of the collection, which by now was partly at Belan and partly at Rug, it was established that many objects filled gaps in the museum's existing collections, besides preserving the history of a unique coastal establishment. There were no objections from the National Museum of Wales and so the Trustees of National Museums and Galleries on Merseyside concluded an agreement with Michael Wynn to buy part of the collection, while certain items, including the boats, were gifts. The moving of the collections took place in the late summer of 1986, and in 1987 an exhibition of most of the collection in the museum's old pilotage building was opened by Michael Wynn. This remained on show until the building was needed to accommodate the new Museum of Liverpool Life in 1993. Many objects still remain on show in the permanent galleries of the Merseyside Maritime Museum, including the restored paddle engines from the yacht *Firefly II* and the figurehead from the barque *William Turner*, while others have been used for research, loans and temporary exhibitions. Some of the tinned food from the 1848 yacht *Vesta* was loaned to the Australian National Maritime Museum, Sydney, in 1998.

Frederick Wynn (1853–1932) about 1920 (21).

Belan Fort itself was eventually sold for development as a series of holiday homes. Planning problems stalled this project and the fort was left to decay. It has been bought recently and the new owners – the Blundells – are hard at work on its restoration. Glynllifon has also witnessed major changes in recent times. The park was opened to visitors with many of its features restored and the estate yard refurbished with craft workshops and a visitor centre. The steam engine that powered the sawmill was put back to working order and the sawmill building was used to house an exhibition on the history of the house and the family. Until 1997 the main house was used as living accommodation and offices for the college. A few pieces of furniture survived, including the pipe organ installed in the first-floor drawing room by Frederick Wynn. A portrait of Vera (née Montague), first wife of the fifth baron, painted by Ms E. M. Wyon in 1920, is the only surviving painting in the house.[34] The house at the time of writing has been sold to a private buyer. Fortunately, the key pieces of the family's history, such as the twin portraits of the first Lord Newborough and Maria Stella, still remain cherished by the family at Rug.

The seventh Lord Newborough, Michael Wynn (1917–1998), who had done so much to preserve the collection, continued to take an interest in it long after its departure to Liverpool. He was especially pleased when the Museum was able to put his uncle's pride and joy, the steam launch *Birdie*, back into commission. His detailed knowledge of Belan Fort and its boats were of immense value when information was being collected for this catalogue.

2 *Belan Fort*

Belan Fort commands the southern entrance of the Menai Straits at a point where the channel is between 300 and 400 yards wide. It stands at the head of a sandy low-lying peninsula which is flanked by the Irish Sea to the west and Foryd Bay, the shallow estuary of the Rivers Foryd and Carrog, to the east. In recent times it has been referred to as 'Fort Belan'. The official visitors' guide by Ivor Wynne Jones in 1979 refers to it as such. The oldest usage is 'Abermenai barracks' which was changed to 'Fort St David' in about 1824 and 'Belan Fort' from about 1840. 'Abermenai barracks' appeared in an account of the building works in 1775 and is used in later documents such as John Spooner's report to Thomas Wynn of a muster there in August 1802. The account of disbursements made by George Bettiss – Thomas John's land agent between 1824 and 1827 – refers to 'Fort St David formerly called the Barracks'.[35] An account for 1836 refers to 'tuning the piano at St David's Fort'.[36] Robert Wynn in his privately published pamphlet of about 1950, used the name Belan Fort, and so did the survey of the Royal Commission for Ancient Monuments.[37] The Wynn collection also contains confirmation in the form of the ribbon of a sailor's boater lettered 'Belan Fort' (see catalogue number 87).

The 672 acres of the Belan Peninsula have been part of the Glynllifon estate and the site of the fort may have an earlier use as a landing place for goods. According to Robert Wynn's account, there was a pen-and-ink sketch in the fort's smoking room dated 1703 showing two warehouses. A tablet dated 1703, possibly from one of these buildings, was re-set in the entrance gate of the fort. Robert Wynn believed that by 1720–30 there was a more substantial residence which was later incorporated into the officers' barracks. Wynne Jones disagreed and felt that the inscription, which was worn, was in fact 1763.

There has been an assumption that work on the fort's walls started in 1775 and its expense was one of the causes of Thomas Wynn's debts. In fact, its first name, Abermenai Barracks, indicates that it was the two barrack blocks which were built before the rest of the fort. John Spooner's letter of 17 August 1802 which described a parade of the Loyal Newborough Volunteers, included a sketch plan of 'the Barriks'. They were two parallel buildings without any fortifying walls. Spooner added measurements of 130 yards inland and 80 at right angles to the buildings and another line of 93

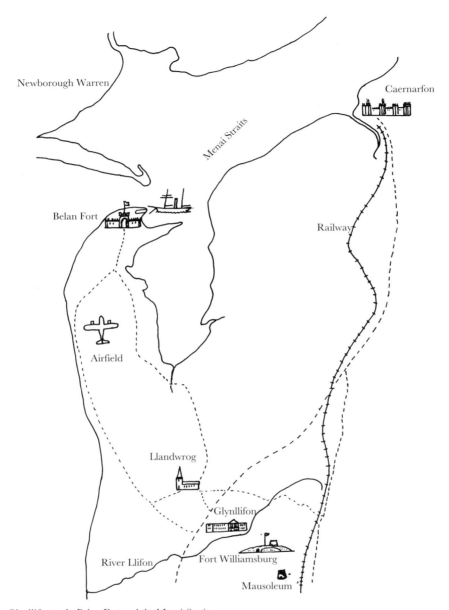

Glynllifon park, Belan Fort and the Menai Straits.

yards following the shoreline, noting that the latter was the best because 'The ground is level and dry'.[38] This shows Thomas Wynn was contemplating a fortified extension to the barracks. His heir had the works carried out between 1824 and 1827. The bills incurred by George Bettiss, the family's land agent, and the large quantities of stone brought in by local sloops suggest that this major project may have included the new dockyard. There

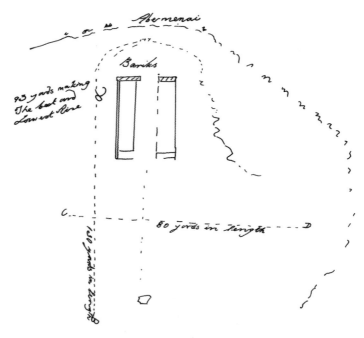

Thomas Spooner's plan of Abermenai Barracks sent to Thomas Wynn, 17 August 1802. (Gwynedd Record Office)

is a possibility that the dockyard was of later date and this is raised by an undated plan and specification for building the new dock at St David's Fort by W. Thomas. From its context the archivist at Gwynedd Record Office has dated it to about 1845, which raises the possibility that the dockyard was built with the *Vesta* in mind.[39]

Sea transport was easier and cheaper than road transport before the mid-nineteenth century. It was common practice to beach cargo vessels or lighter cargoes ashore from anchorages at places where there were no quays. Belan Point is nearer to Glynllifon than the port of Caernarfon, and it is not inconceivable that bulk cargoes such as coal were delivered there.[40] There is plenty of evidence in the Newborough archives of many shipments by sea in the early nineteenth century. In July 1831, for example, the estate accounts recorded coal delivered by the *Jane* and *Alice* and sail canvas by the *Zephyr*.[41] However, it is unclear whether they discharged at Belan or Caernarfon. The Straits with the 'head port' of Beaumaris saw an increasing traffic with slate, stone, timber and agricultural produce outward and coal and 'general cargo' inward.[42] The latter included luxury goods and guns for the fort sent from Liverpool and London.[43]

Belan Fort had greater strategic significance than Fort Williamsburg because of its position. It protected the southern entrance of the Menai

Belan Fort and dockyard from the air. (Arthur Pickett, now Michael Connolly Photography, Chester)

Straits against enemy attack. This meant not just invasion or amphibious raiding parties but privateers. There was such a threat after France entered the war on the American colonists' side in 1778, followed by Spain and the Netherlands the following year, with the resulting British loss of command of the sea. The American colonists, while having to build a navy from nothing, could capture British merchant ships by means of privateers – armed merchantmen. This guerrilla war at sea not only deprived the enemy of resources, it induced fear, uncertainty and a depression in morale because of its randomness and the element of surprise.[44] The Irish Sea was an attractive cruising ground for the privateers because it had a large concentration of shipping sailing to and from the major ports of Bristol, Dublin and Liverpool, all using the southern entrance to gain the open ocean. There was also a high volume of trade along the coast and to the Irish ports.

The plan of the fort reflects this role of defending the entrance to the Straits. It is oblong with salients on the north and south sides. The north is a gun battery with embrasures for fourteen guns overlooking the Straits. This

Belan Fort interior, with officers' accommodation on the left and other ranks to the right, in about 1850–5.

substantial earthwork with stone retaining walls enabled fire to be directed out to sea across the channel or into the Straits in a 150° arc. The south salient defended the fort and its main entrance on the landward side. This consisted of a gateway with a gun battery over it leading to a drawbridge over a dry moat. The main gatehouse also contained two gun ports. The outer walls were crenellated and carried a walkway and at the south-west and south-east angles there were two circular defensive positions that could provide covering fire for the south salient entrance and for the east and west walls. All the walls were 12 feet high and faced in stone. In the centre there were two barrack blocks. The officers' accommodation was on the west side with other ranks on the east side along with a separate stable block. There were ancillary buildings to the north and south sides including a bakery, stables and coach house. The north side contained two ammunition stores and a central gatehouse leading to the gun battery. From about 1890 it was surmounted by a wooden look-out. The whole fort was surrounded by a 10-foot outer stone wall that linked it with the dockyard. This wall could be the work of Spencer Wynn in about 1840, 'who was mad on building walls and built one on any pretext whatever, whether it be round his residences at Glynllifon and Belan, or any farmhouse!'[45]

The nearest coastal fort in both date and distance was Fort Perch Rock, erected at New Brighton to defend the Mersey between 1825 and 1828. It was designed by Captain John Kitson of the Royal Engineers and was a trapezoidal shape with gun batteries on three sides in casemates and two Martello-type towers on the landward side. His design reflected the experience of fortification in the Napoleonic Wars.[46] Spencer Wynn's battery was unprotected and yet, given the narrowness of the Menai Straits, could have given a good account if ever called to action. But the crenellations of the defending walls reflect an older tradition going back to the Middle Ages. While the fort could have defended the Straits, there was not even the remotest threat from the French or any other nation at the time of building. Fort St David's must have been therefore as much a leisure activity as a military installation.

Nevertheless, its predecessor the Barracks was used as a military base for defending the coast. Thomas Wynn assembled the Caernarfonshire militia on 27 September 1776 at 'Abermenai barracks' and early in 1778 he received the king's warrant dated 26 March to mobilize them.[47] After embodiment, the regiment marched to Holyhead for garrison duties. In June 1779 the regiment was serving in Kent and by 1782 was stationed in Essex as part of the forces arrayed against a French invasion. At the end of the war it moved back to Wales and was disbanded. It is presumed that Thomas Wynn made his own arrangements to maintain a watch at Abermenai (possibly with his unofficial Fort Williamsburg garrison) until his departure for Italy in 1782.

The outbreak of war with the revolutionary government of France in 1793 saw the re-embodiment of the county militia. It served away from Caernarfonshire from 1793 to 1801 and from 1803 to 1814, including the campaigns in Spain and Portugal. The threat of a French invasion led to legislation in 1794 for the strengthening of the militia and the formation of volunteer corps for local defence. The volunteer movement was stimulated by the abortive French expedition that landed at Fishguard in February 1797. Companies and whole battalions were raised by officers commissioned by the king or the lord lieutenant. The 1798 Defence of the Realm Act obliged the lord lieutenants to compile lists of able-bodied men aged between fifteen and sixty, with the kinds of military and non-military tasks they were capable of carrying out. This led to the formation of Armed Associations for local defence and auxiliary work such as acting as constables and lookouts. Thomas Wynn raised the Loyal Newborough Volunteer Association, comprising seventeen officers, thirty non-commissioned officers, five drummers and 320 privates in companies.[48] The Peace of Amiens of 1802 meant they could stand down and the parade of 17 August 1802 only contained twenty-six men.[49] They were reformed under the 1802 Volunteer Act on 27 August 1803 as the Loyal Newborough Infantry Volunteers, with an extra company of a hundred volunteers. The latter were mainly Lord Newborough's tenants, who agreed to serve without pay and any of the other privileges of a volunteer. The costs of this extra company were paid directly by Lord Newborough.[50] The battle of Trafalgar in 1805 destroyed French naval power and hence the ability to invade the United Kingdom. The corps was stood down finally in 1808. A silver medal of merit awarded to an unknown volunteer was displayed at the fort.[51] The weapons paid for by Lord Newborough were returned to either Belan or Williamsburg and this is shown by a receipt dated 5 March 1810 from Margaret Jones, executrix of Richard Thomas Smith, for £16. 3s. 9d. for cleaning the muskets of the Loyal Newborough Volunteers.[52] Apart from the objects preserved in the Wynn Collection, the Museum of the Royal Welsh Fusiliers in Caernarfon Castle contains a cross belt plate and officer's uniform buttons.[53]

After the completion of the fort, it became the centre of summer leisure activities including sailing and firing the guns. There was also a residential caretaker cum boatman. When Glynllifon burnt down in 1836, Spencer Wynn and his family lived at the fort while their main home was being rebuilt. A book of pressed seaweed, dated 1842 and now in the Botany Department of Liverpool Museum, is from this period. Frederick Wynn had a particular affection for the fort, 'and when he was in residence at Glynllifon seldom a day passed, winter or summer when he did not go to visit it in the afternoon. He made no structural alterations, but fortunately being interested in the relics of the past, he carefully kept all that he had found'.[54]

Robert Wynn and his family used the fort for their summer holidays. According to the late Michael Wynn, this was a major expedition from Rug, involving a lorry to carry luggage and provisions that travelled at a stately fifteen miles an hour. At the outbreak of the Second World War the fort and the peninsula were occupied for military purposes. There was a coastal battery and the entrance channel was protected with sunken mines that could be detonated from the fort. The Straits and their seaward approach were patrolled by six motor boats which were based at the moorings off the dockyard. In the surrounding area, a training camp for the Twenty-Third Armoured Brigade was established and this was followed by the building at Llandwrog of a training base for bomber crews. This became operational in the summer of 1941. This in turn led to the stationing of two RAF air-sea rescue launches at the dockyard. The airfield was closed in 1945. It was used for the storage of nerve gas bombs and these were finally disposed of by dumping at sea between 1951 and 1955. A special concrete landing strip was built near the fort for tank landing craft to carry these lethal weapons out to sea.[55]

3 Ordnance, Munitions and Other Military Equipment

The original complement of guns is not known. Based on the number of embrasures, there could have been eighteen, with fourteen in the main battery and two each for the gatehouse and the landward battery. At the time of the sale in 1986 there were thirty pieces listed:

  two thirty-two pounder
  nine twenty-four pounder marked with the cyphers of George III and George IV
  eight twelve pounder
  seven 'carronades'
  two three pounder
  one twelve pounder (field gun).[56]

The Wynn Collection includes five 'carronades' which are in fact cannon. There was another taken to Rug along with the two brass signal guns from the *Vesta*. The thirty-twos and probably the twenty-fours were bought by Frederick Wynn from Pembroke Dock in 1892.[57] The original guns may have been moved from Fort Williamsburg and appear to have been the twelve pounders or the 'carronades' which can be seen in the photographs of the battery about 1850–5, and were still *in situ* in 1986. The main subject of the 1850–5 photograph was an impressive twelve pounder field gun, which by 1986 had lost a wheel. The same photograph also shows a mortar of the type used by Captain Manby for throwing lines to shipwrecks.[58] The guns continued to be fired after the Volunteers had been disbanded. There were salutes for important visiting vessels such as the Trinity House yacht carrying Admiral Collinson in 1875 and there were other occasions such as royal anniversaries which were marked by gun salutes in that intensely patriotic era.

This tradition was carried on by the family and latterly, in 1969, the fort marked the investiture of the prince of Wales at Caernarfon with a thirty-one-gun salute. The guns were also fired for pleasure. This pastime was not unique. The duke of Portland equipped his pleasure barge on Ullswater with six brass cannon for producing a stupendous echo from the surrounding hills; in 1778 Joseph Pocklington bought Derwent Isle on Derwent Water and built among other things a fort equipped with cannon.[59] This custom was

The main battery in about 1850–1855.

maintained and became part of the list of attractions when the fort was opened to visitors in 1978. This could lead to problems if there were boats in the vicinity. In 1969 during the celebration of the prince of Wales's investiture at Caernarfon, the then husband of Princess Margaret, Anthony Armstrong-Jones, was almost hit by flying wadding when arriving at Belan by boat and in 1976 Michael Wynn was fined for causing damage to a yacht's sail. In the days of sail when there were hundreds of wooden sailing ships passing the Welsh coast bound for Liverpool or the Straits, shipwrecks were common. If a vessel was spotted ashore near the fort, the guns were fired to alert the authorities and the lifeboat situated at Llanddwyn Island on the Anglesey shore.[60]

1. Cannon ('carronades') (5)

Acc. No. 1986.201.213–17

These five pieces were part of a collection of twelve cannon displayed in No. 3 Boat Store at the dockyard. All five are mounted on wooden naval gun carriages. They have been described as carronades and indeed they share the same design of muzzle. But the carronade which was developed and cast by the Carron Iron Works, near Falkirk, from 1778 was a shorter weapon with a swivel instead of trunnions. No. 1 is marked as being by the Falkirk Iron

Company. This company started between 1817 and 1820 and produced many cast-iron articles including cannon between four and eighteen pounders for merchant ships. These are all twelve pounders and No. 5 is proof-marked as such. They are also so similar in style to No. 1 that the chances are that, although they are not marked 'Falkirk', they were cast by that foundry. Although technically not carronades they would have had similar ballistic characteristics, that is, the accurate projection of roundshot to ranges of 400 to 600 yards. A four pounder of the same make and design was trawled up in the Firth of Forth in 1968 and conserved by the National Museum of Antiquities (later the Royal Scottish Museum) in 1968.[61] Their date of manufacture after 1817–20 suggests that they may have been part of the original battery and this is reinforced by the fact that they were 'retired' to No. 3 Boat Store. However, it is not clear where they were positioned because the 1850–5 photographs of the north battery only show the twelve pounder land guns that were still there in 1986. It is also worth noting that similar short-barrelled pieces can be found at another local landed family's home – Plas Newydd, Llanfair Pwllgwyngyll, Anglesey.

2. 'Signal' cannon (3)

Acc. No. 1986.201.237.1–3

These three pieces measure 6 inches (152 mm) in overall length and have a bore of $^{15}/_{16}$ inches (19 mm). They are of cast iron and of a similar design to larger late eighteenth-century cannon. They are mounted in more recent wooden mounts and fitted with turned wooden tompions. They appear to have been made for mounting in a swivel and could have been fitted on one of the family's early boats. A similar type was fitted to the Manx schooner yacht *Peggy*, preserved at the Nautical Museum, Castletown.[62] It is possible they came from the schooner *Mermaid* of 1795.

3. Ramrod and worm

Acc. No. 1986.201.211–12

The ramrod was used to push home the charge of gunpowder and wadding down the gun's barrel. This worm with its screw was used to extract fragments of the charge including the burnt paper of the cartridge. Other gunner's equipment included a sponge for cleaning out the barrel after firing, to ensure any burning fragments were extinguished, a scoop for powder if paper cartridges were not employed, a linstock for holding a slow match and a portfire holder for firing the touchhole.[63]

The main entrance and drawbridge. (Crown copyright: RCAHMW)

4. Gunner's quadrant

Acc. No. 1986.201.221

This was used for measuring the angle of elevation of a gun's barrel. It was applied to the barrel and the angle was measured by a plumbob which is missing. It is stored in a wooden case. 'Gunner's quadrant' is written in ink on this case in the same hand as found on other items associated with the steam yacht *Vesta*. A quadrant is listed along with a chronometer and a barometer in her inventory but this suggests that it was a navigational instrument not this artillery device. It is inscribed Watkins, London, who could be either Francis Watkins of 5 Charing Cross, working between 1747 and 1784, or William Watkins, 21 St James's, 1784 to 1809.[64] Its date suggests that it was part of the equipment of the Loyal Newborough Volunteer Association or the county militia.

5. Slow matches and portfires

Acc. No. 1986.201.219

Slow matches were made of 'three loosely woven strands of hemp boiled in the lees of old wine, or in a solution of wood ash or saltpetre, the whole being bound with an outer layer of hemp strands'.[65] These fourteen complete and three incomplete matches are treated with pitch and could have been made at the fort.

The portfire was carried on a staff – a linstock. The flame of the slow match was transferred to the touchhole by the portfire which was a stiff tube made of layers of paper. These ten examples are heavily waxed and are stored in a box which originally housed a telescope.

6. Photographs of the gun battery, *c.*1850–5

Acc. No. 1986.201.272 Archive Ref. D/WYN/7/3

These two photographs are part of a series of nine albumen prints showing the fort, the dockyard and one of Fort Williamsburg. The first view is to the west and includes a small mortar, possibly for line throwing and a wheeled ammunition store in the foreground. The latter still survived in 1986, though in a disintegrating state. Beyond there is the flagpole which is shown flying the Red Ensign in a view of the parade ground and barracks. There are three of the original guns mounted on naval carriages and a field gun visible. The latter is attended by two people, one of whom is bearded and wearing a cheese cutter cap and holding the sponge for the gun. The second figure is in the act of putting the linstock to the touchhole. A third figure, in a short brass-buttoned uniform jacket and white duck trousers, holds a flag.

The field gun is the main subject of the second picture with the same people and looking east. The man in the dark suit and cap is posed with the sponge while the other, who is side on, wears a bowler hat and an overcoat not dissimilar to those in the collection (see No. 147). The third man holds the flag at the eastern end of the battery. The gun's equipment included two cooper-made buckets with sloping sides hung from its axle. There is a smaller example in the collection (Acc. No. 1986.201.104). Similar examples can be found in early nineteenth-century deck scenes on naval vessels. In Christie's auction of 23 October 1987, lot 206 was similar but described as a salt bucket.

7. Round shot and casting patterns

Acc. Nos. 1986.201.210 and 246

The No. 3 Dockyard Store contained a large number of 6 and 9 lb. cast-iron cannon balls for use in the gun battery's carronades and possibly for the *Vesta's* four brass guns. Six casks were carried on board.[66] The stock must have been depleted by artillery exercises and the four wooden patterns could be sent to a foundry to make replacements. In the nineteenth century, this was likely to have been the Union Foundry at Caernarfon. In 1854 it was taken over by J. P. de Winton, a relative by marriage to Spencer Wynn.

8. Chain shot

Acc. No. 1986.201.238

This consists of two cast-iron hemispheres linked by a short chain. It was used to destroy the standing rigging of sailing ships, and as an anti-personnel device.

9. Grapeshot

Acc. No. 1986.201.218

This was so-called from the projective's resemblance to a bunch of grapes. These examples are quilted grapeshot. The bullets are sewn into a canvas bag and tied up with quilting line. This form was replaced by 'tier grapeshot' in the mid-nineteenth century, in which the bullets were arranged on three tiers separated by iron plates. It was usually an anti-personnel weapon.

10. Box of wads

Acc. No. 1986.201.220

Wads were made from old rope yarns or, in this case, tarred twine wrapped around a core of hay or oakum. They helped make the bore of the gun gas tight, which maximized the power of the gunpowder.

One wad was rammed home on top of the charge of gunpowder before the round shot was loaded. A second was rammed on top of the shot. The box contains wads for twelve pounders and it has 'No. 3 Cartridge Chest' painted on the lid. The style of the lettering suggests it was part of the fort's original equipment.

11. Gunpowder casks (2) and tins (2)

Acc. No. 1986.201.269

The two casks measure 14½ inches (368 mm) and 17¾ inches (450 mm) high, with lid diameters of 11¼ inches (285 mm) and 10½ inches (267 mm) respectively. They are fitted with copper hoops to avoid the risks of causing sparks. There is also a separate lid branded 'T. & S. Sharp' with a card label attached: 'Sharp's Gunpowder Mills, Office 59 King William Street, London', and it is addressed to 'Lord Newborough, Glyn, Caernarvon'.

Gunpowder like many other supplies and equipment was purchased from London suppliers, and the capital was supplied by manufacturers in Kent and Surrey who had access to oak for charcoal and imported saltpetre. The two tins, which are probably later than the casks, were for finer powders for personal weapons and were supplied by the Guildford Co. and John Hall of Faversham, Kent.

The main battery in 1953, with Frederick Wynn's watch house over the north gate.
(Crown copyright: RCAHMW)

12. Cutlasses (3)

Acc. No. 1986.201.222.1–3

These are plain examples of the cutlass type of naval officer's fighting sword
of the sort introduced about 1825. They have a simple knuckle bow hilt in
brass with a sharkskin wire-bound grip and with leather brass-mounted
scabbards. They are marked 'W. Parker, maker to His Majesty, Holborn,
London'. They are mounted in a circular wooden block ornamented with
brass stampings for use as a wall decoration. W. Parker supplied Spencer
Wynn with carbines in 1834 and these may have been supplied at the same
time. The *Vesta* carried swords as well as muskets.[67]

13. Flintlock carbines (3), flints and cartridges

Acc. Nos. 1986.201.224.1–3, 226, 227.1–3

Carbines were smooth-bore short-barrelled weapons, useful for naval
engagements. These were made by W. Parker, Holborn (1790–1840), who
was one of London's leading gun-makers and who held a Royal Warrant. He
is not recorded as making carbines. One has no ramrod. The box of flints has

been 'knapped' to make a square shape with a sharp edge to produce the necessary spark. The cartridges (in three boxes) consist of a paper wrapper with the lead ball tied into one end. They have not been filled with powder.

14. Percussion cap carbines (3)

Acc. No. 1986.201.225.1–3

These three were made by Parker Field & Sons of London and date from between 1850 and 1886. It is likely they were made about 1850 as part of the outfit of the *Vesta*. Percussion cap weapons were an advance on flintlocks and used a small copper foil 'cap' filled with powder to detonate the main charge.

15. Bayonets (49)

Acc. No. 1986.201–8

Among the forty-nine bayonets, there are five types. A single example of the Land Pattern for the Long Land musket, dating from about 1730–40, is the oldest. The second is a single example of a Land Pattern bayonet of about 1760–80 for the short Land Musket manufactured by Samuel Dawes of High Street, Birmingham. The third type and the bulk of the collection is of the India Pattern of 1795–1800. These are similar to the 1760–80 Land Pattern but stamped with an official inspection mark of a crowned '6' or '5'. Some also have rack numbers and clearly date from the establishment of the Loyal Newborough Volunteer Association. There are two later types. The first is an 1839 variant, which was for a privately made percussion musket of the government type and calibre (.753 inch) but without the Hanoverian locking catch. The second is the carbine/fusil bayonet. These were used on many variations of carbines or carbine smooth-bore fusils from about 1750 to 1840. 'G.S.' stamped on the blade denotes George Salter of Birmingham. His earliest reference is 1816–17 and by 1854 he was at work in West Bromwich. It is likely that this was for use with the Parker Field percussion carbines on the *Vesta*.

16. Powder flasks (8)

Acc. No. 1986.201.223.1–8

These eight flasks are of varying designs which reflect the family's military and sporting shooting. They probably date from between 1790 and 1850. Numbers 1 to 3 are of the Sykes type, with the first made of copper, the others of tin plate. The third also has a graduated nozzle to deliver specified amounts of powder. The fourth is in red painted tin plate with paper labels printed 'John Hall, Faversham and London, rifle powder'. The remainder are made of moulded leather. Number 6 is embossed with a hunting scene and number 7 has a graduated nozzle dispensing either 1 or 1 ¼ ounces. Number 8 has lost its nozzle and has 'FT 1818' and '74 C[H]' scratched on both sides.

17. Shoulder pouch

Acc. No. 1986.201.229

This leather pouch would have been worn on its cross belt diagonally across the chest by the artillery section of the Loyal Newborough Association. It has been dated to about 1800.[68] It carries a brass cartouche badge in two parts of two crossed cannon surmounted by a grenade. The belt carries a lion's mask badge in brass.

18. Drums (2)

Acc. Nos. 1986.201.230 and 231

Drums were essential to communicate changes in manœuvre at a period when infantry were drilled and deployed in tight formations. These two drums were probably supplied for the Loyal Newborough Association. The first, which has been refurbished by NMGM, is painted yellow with red, white and blue diagonal stripes on the bands at each end. There is a belted and crowned red cartouche surrounded by roses and thistles. If there was an inscription, this has been worn off. There is no maker's name or label. It is of similar construction to the town of Greenock's drum in the collection of the McLean Museum and Art Gallery, Greenock. There are two turned wooden drumsticks of unequal length which suggests they were from different instruments.

The drum (18) of the Loyal Newborough Volunteer Association.

The second drum is completely plain and riveted with domed brass studs. The lower skin is missing, but inside it carries a paper label of Robert Horne, drum-maker to George III of 20 Barbican, London. According to the London trade directories, Horne's business was active between about 1790 and 1800. The Dockyard Museum at the fort also displayed a horn, bugles, key bugle and an oboe from the band of the Association.

19. Standard of the Loyal Newborough Volunteer Association

Acc. No. 1986.201.245

The Royal Commission's survey of Fort Williamsburg mentions that the main room of the headquarters' building contained, when visited, a military

The standard (19) of the Loyal Newborough Volunteer Association.

museum containing 'quantities of flint-lock and percussion-cap muskets and the standard of the "Newborough Association" '.[69] Owen also refers to the colours of the Association being preserved at Fort Williamsburg 'which bore in addition to the Arms of Wynne of Glynllifon, a scroll inscribed "Loyal Newborough Association" '.[70] Among the items from Belan Fort was a square woollen cloth similar to the flag bunting crudely stretched on a wooden frame. The family coat of arms was painted on both sides of the dark blue woollen cloth. All sides have been hemmed and there are grommets on one of the vertical edges by which it could be attached to its staff.

The family also own an interesting framed letter written by John McMahon from Carlton House on 17 November 1800 on behalf of the Prince Regent, expressing 'approbation of your Lordship's praiseworthy exertions in the County of Carnarvon' and 'the Prince has ordered Colours to be immediately prepared for that Distinguished Corps, which His Royal Highness intends your Lordship will have the goodness to present, in his name, for their acceptance'.

4 Decorative Objects

This section includes the two busts of Thomas Wynn and Maria Stella which must have been at Glynllifon. Other more mundane objects were part of the furnishings of the fort's main house (formerly the officers' accommodation). The two ship carvings date from the family's residence at the fort between 1836 and 1848.

20. Busts of Thomas Wynn, first Baron Newborough, and Maria Stella, second Lady Newborough

Acc. Nos. 1986.201.183 and 184

Modelled in plaster, with a later painted inscription on their pedestals, these depict the first Lord Newborough and his second wife, Maria Stella, after their return to Glynllifon from Italy in 1793. Lord Newborough is shown in Roman fashion with a toga around his shoulders. His wife's costume and hairstyle owes more to contemporary fashion, an Empire gown with a loose high waist and a plunging neckline.[71] The works are not signed and the sculptor has not been identified. It is likely that they were modelled from life, probably while the couple were in residence in their house at Portland Place. They are almost certainly the originals and not copies of busts carved in stone. It is possible that they were commissioned around the same time as a pair of full-length oil portraits dated 1802. Both busts were displayed at the dockyard from 1977 with a display of Volunteer equipment and arms.

21. Portrait of the Hon. Frederick Wynn (1853–1932)

Acc. No. 1986.201.182

The portrait is painted in oil on canvas by an unknown artist. From the appearance of the sitter (and perhaps emphasized by the deep fur collar of his overcoat) it probably dates from the last decade of his life. It is not listed in Steegman's catalogue of portraits at Glynllifon and it would have been appropriate either at Belan Fort or Boduan. The latter was the original Wynn family home before Thomas Wynn's marriage to Frances Glynne of Glynllifon. It was held in great affection by Frederick who was a regular visitor. His diary from 1876 to 1878 survives in the Newborough archive at Gwynedd Record Office, starting when he was twenty-one. It shows that much of his routine revolved around these two places, along with visits to his cousins at Rug. He also recorded the weather and his shooting and fishing activities. There were also regular visits to London where he socialized with friends, went to the theatre, the Zoo, the Royal Academy and shopping. He had also developed his taste for scientific gadgets and an interest in engineering. On 2 January 1875, he gave a magic lantern show for 'the working classes' in the village school about London Zoo, and on 17 February he gave 'a fine performance in the evening with the Arphengescope in the large drawing room'. Two days earlier he attended the testing of steamship *Brecon*'s engines at de Winton's foundry at Caernarfon.[72] This was perhaps the start of his infatuation with steam engines.

22. Drawing of Glynllifon House

Acc. No. 1986.201.181

A charcoal sketch on paper of the frontage of the house from the far side of the River Llifon. It shows the west wing added between 1889 and 1893. There is no signature or date, and it could be the work of one of the members of the family.

23. Drawing of HMS *Vernon*

Acc. No. 1986.201.270

Pen, ink and wash on paper signed by William Huggins (1781–1845), dated August 1832, view towards the port bow at anchor with the guns run out. HMS *Vernon* was a 50-gun frigate of 2,082 tons launched in 1832 at Woolwich. Huggins was a noted and prolific marine artist who had served at sea with the East India Company until 1814. He exhibited widely in London, including the Royal Academy. Edward Duncan, his son-in-law, engraved his work and gave it a wide distribution. This is possibly one of Frederick Wynn's purchases, perhaps along with the model of HMS *Pike* (see no. 51).

24. Crown of Bardsey

Acc. No. 1986.201.180 (Photo Archive No. D/WYN/7/37)

Bardsey Island (Ynys Enlli) lies off the south shore of the Llŷn Peninsula and was owned by the family until 1971. Maria Stella is credited with the invention of the imaginary Kingdom of Bardsey and the senior man of the island was crowned in 1826. This crown, however, was made at the work-shops of Trinity House at Holyhead and presented to King Love Pritchard by Captain Jarrett of Trinity House in 1925. The latter organization was responsible for the lighthouse on the island. The crown is fashioned from sheet iron painted gold with suitable 'celtic' motifs beaten into it.

The Bardsey Crown worn by Love Pritchard, 1925 (24).

25. Bust of Lord Nelson

Acc. Nos. 1986.201.166 and 167

This is a moulded salt-glazed stoneware spirit bottle by Doulton & Watt of about 1830. It is one of the many objects commemorating Nelson and his heroic death at the battle of Trafalgar in 1805. A framed modern copy of Nelson's prayer before the battle hung in the main house at the fort.

26. Models of sailors (8)

Acc. Nos. 1986.201.187.1–8

These eight models of sailors of the Victorian Royal Navy are made of papier mâché and plaster, and formed part of a larger set displayed in the entrance hall of the main house. They are all in the uniforms introduced by the Royal Navy in 1857. Numbers 1, 3, 5 and 6 are in blue serge jumpers and trousers, and 2, 4, 7 and 8 are in white cotton duck. All wear the issue straw hats which are similar to the one in the collection (see no. 145). Number 1 has a stoker's badge, 3 and 5 are a gunner and gunner's mate, and 8 is a petty officer with two good conduct stripes.

27. Pipe racks (3)

Acc. No. 1986.201.175

These are carved and painted in the form of a White Ensign with three loops, each to hold pipes. Two were fixed on either side of the mantelpiece in the study of the main house.

28. Fireplace ornaments (2)

Acc. No. 1986.201.176

These two sailor figures are cast in aluminium. The first depicts a young sailor in Royal Naval dress leaning against a capstan and the second a bearded sailor also from the Royal Navy, cutlass in hand, standing with his back to a ship's wheel. Both their plinths have 'Britannia's Pride' cast in them. Aluminium was a fairly scarce metal until about 1900, which suggests that these were purchased by Frederick Wynn.

29. Stern carving from the ship *Jane*

Acc. No. 1986.201.101

The American ship *Jane*, bound for Liverpool with a cargo of cotton, ran aground on a lee shore off Belan on 18 June 1840. She did not break up immediately and Captain Cook from Virginia camped in the dunes while the

The stern carving from the American sailing ship Jane, wrecked 1840 (29).

valuable cargo was salvaged. Spencer Wynn obtained her splendid stern carving before her remains were blown up because of their danger to other ships.[73]

The carving depicts an American eagle with outstretched wings standing over the stars and stripes on an inclined shield and carrying the motto 'e pluribus unum' painted on a scroll in its beak. The central subject is perched on an elaborate curled leaf design incorporating two stars, with carved ropework below. This patriotic emblem was a common ornament on nineteenth-century American sailing ships. It dates from its adoption as a national symbol in 1783. The eagle was the personification of the Greek god Zeus, and a native species – the bald-headed eagle – was adopted by the classically educated founding fathers of the United States. Thereafter there was a mania for eagles decorating everything from buildings to quilts and ships.

The carving was displayed in No. 3 Boathouse until it was moved to Liverpool. The original paintwork and gilding is still intact and it is one of the finest examples of American ship carving to be preserved.

30. Figurehead of the barque *William Turner*

Acc. No. 1986.201.102

The *William Turner* was on the last few days of a long passage from Ichaboe on the Peruvian coast with a cargo of guano for Liverpool. The guano, from the millions of seabirds inhabiting the west coast and off-shore islands of South America, was a prized fertilizer rich in nitrate. On the 10 January 1845, she was off the Smalls lighthouse on the Pembrokeshire coast, when a strong gale from WSW to SSW blew up and continued until midnight on 12 January.[74] The barque failed to weather Anglesey, possibly because her master had been unable to fix her position, and she drove ashore in

Figurehead of the barque William Turner, *wrecked 1845 (30).*

Caernarfon Bay with the loss of all hands. The guns of Belan were not heard by the pilot station at Llanddwyn and it caused some controversy in the port of Caernarfon and pressure for the Harbour Trustees to place a light at Llanddwyn. The wreckage was strewn along the beach from Abermenai to Llanddwyn and a Mr Edwards, a diver from Menai Bridge, was able to salvage a large quantity of rope, equipment and presumably this figurehead (unless it had been washed off) before blowing up the upturned hull.[75]

The *William Turner* was a wooden barque of 488 tons, built at Greenock in 1833, owned by Campbell & Co., and registered at Belfast. There appears to be no connection with the William Turner (1766–1853) of Caernarfon who did so much to develop local slate trade and shipping. This is a standing full-length figure in contemporary gentleman's dress of tailcoat, tight buff trousers with foot straps.[76] Although the figure is undoubtedly eponymous, the family have always affectionately known him as Nelson. Standing figureheads were popular in the early nineteenth century, although they were more expensive and more vulnerable than a head and shoulders bust. Shipowners often named new vessels after themselves, their wives, daughters, relatives, friends or partners.

5 *Domestic Equipment*

A representative selection of domestic equipment was acquired to reflect the life at the fort and on board the yacht *Vesta*. In many cases it is not possible to decide whether a particular item came from the fort or the yacht. The brass water heater (see no. 155) definitely came from the *Vesta*, but in all other cases the yacht's inventories and those of her predecessor, the *Sapphire*, are not specific enough to be entirely certain.[77]

31. Kettles (4)

Acc. Nos. 1986.201.255.1–2, 256 and 262

Two are of the 'ship kettle' type designed to be permanently placed on a range with a tap for discharging the hot water. Number 1 is in copper and the second in brass with a tap stamped 'Hickman'. 'Ship's kettles' were not necessarily confined to ships and could be used wherever a large quantity of hot water was needed – in a barracks kitchen for example. It is possible that one or both were part of the outfit of the fort and it is worth noting that the inventory of the militia's equipment stored at Fort Williamsburg in 1773 included '3 hampers of canteens and kettles'.

There are also two more conventional 'hand' kettles. The first is square in shape and the second is double-skinned.

32. Kitchenware (31)

Acc. Nos. 1986.201.263, 258, 206 and 266

This includes tinware which was painted with aluminium paint in recent times to conceal the rust that had penetrated the tin coating. This suggests that it is some age and could be part of the outfit of the *Vesta*. It comprises: two roasting tins, ten serving dishes or basins, one coffee pot, one soup tureen, one whisk and twelve shaving mugs with handles. Twelve shaving mugs were supplied to the *Vesta* in 1848 and it is likely by association that the whole group came from this yacht. The rest consists of one griddle, one cast-iron meat dish, one soup ladle and one pewter sugar basin.[78]

33. Wooden platters (7)

Acc. Nos. 1986.201.14.1–7

These seven circular platters have turned raised rim and are branded on the back with an 'N' and a crown. Each one has individual initials as well: one 'EJH', two 'RJ' and a compass rose, three 'JR', four 'G', five 'H', six 'JM' and seven 'JJ/11'. They could be from the *Vesta* which had four wooden dishes for the crew in 1849–51, or part of the Volunteers' utensils.

34. Ceramic ware (4)

Acc. Nos. 1986.201.188.1–2, 189, and 190

This again is a miscellany with two heavily repaired gravy boats and a sugar-bowl cover all made by the Royal Worcester Pottery. They carry the family crest and date from the late nineteenth century. The first one has been riveted, which suggests it and its companion pieces were 'cast offs' from Glynllifon. There is also a tea plate from the Royal Clyde Yacht Club by Minton which probably dates from the cruises of Frederick Wynn's yachts after 1891.

35. Pewter beakers (8)

Acc. No. 1986.201.43

These eight beakers are stamped with three lions on the rim and 'Alderson' on the inside. Alderson was a pewterer and lead merchant, who was listed in the London trade directories between 1816 and 1860. They were displayed in the entrance hall of the main house.

36. Water breakers (2)

Acc. Nos. 1986.201.103.1–2

These two are small oval casks with brass hoops used to store water in ships' lifeboats. There are no clues as to their origin, but their pristine condition suggests they were always displayed in the main house of the fort rather than being taken to sea.

37. Self-acting cooking box

Acc. No. 1986.201.169

This 'Norwegian self cooking apparatus and simple refrigerator' was manufactured by the Piston Machine & Ice Company, 301–303 Oxford Street, London. The manufacturer's dates have not been traced and it is probable that the Oxford Street address was no more than a retail shop. It

Some examples of domestic equipment: a. self-acting cooking box (37); b. water breaker (36); c. water heater from Vesta *(1); d. tin ware including 'shaving mugs', coffee pot, serving dishes and bowl (32); e. ship's brass kettle.*

consists of a stout wooden box with a hinged lid fitted with closely packed hay in a woollen cloth as insulation. There are two tinplate food containers. It worked by the 'hay box' method and was the kind of gadget that would have appealed to Frederick Wynn.

38. Ice box

Acc. No. 1986.201.170

This was made by the Wenham Lake Ice Company of 125 The Strand, London. The company, which was of American origin, could not be traced in the London trade directories. It consists of an insulated wooden box with a galvanized ice container. There are rings on each side for lashing it down to a deck. Its size and that of the cooking box would have made them suitable for day excursions in one of Frederick Wynn's boats. There was an ice house at Glynllifon and ice was imported to the United Kingdom from the Baltic and North America in increasing quantities from the early 1840s.

39. Tinned provisions (12)

Acc. Nos. 1986.201.50.1–12

Of the twelve tins, there are four large and two small of cod fish, three of chicken broth and three of dried yeast. According to their labels they were all from Henry Gamble & Company, 137 Leadenhall Street, London, manufactured at Morrison's Quay, Cork, prize-winner at the Great Exhibition, 1851. The 'canisters' are made from heavy gauge tinplate and the flanged lid is soldered in place with the air being evacuated from an aperture in the top. The opening instructions call for a hammer and cold chisel! The principle of 'canning' as a method of food preservation was established by François Appert, a Paris confectioner in 1795. The use of tinplate canisters was patented in England by Peter Durand in 1810. In 1812, Donkin Hall & Gamble's Preservatory was established at J. & E. Hall's Ironworks at Dartford. They supplied soups and foodstuffs to the Royal Navy and these were tested on the Baffin Bay expedition in 1814 and Parry's North-West Passage expedition in 1819. By 1847 tinned preserved beef was part of the standard naval rations. The earliest surviving tins are the two preserved at the Hull Maritime Museum's collection. Parry's 1825 expedition left some tins on the ice after the loss of HMS *Fury*. These were probably picked up by a Hull whaler, possibly in 1833, and a tin of beef and one of pea soup were eventually presented to the Museum at Hull. They were opened about 1919 and the contents eaten without any fatal effects![79] The *Vesta* carried tinned food. The first stock was supplied by Goldner of London, a rival supplier to the Royal Navy to Gambles, and the second inventory for 1849–51 lists two tins of chicken broth and eleven of dried yeast. It is likely that the surviving tins are the residue of the provisions taken ashore for storage when the *Vesta* was laid up.

40. Bottle of Grimwade's patent desiccated milk

Acc. No. 1986.201.268

This was prepared by the Desiccated Milk Company (Limited), Sheepmate Farm, Harrow on the Hill, Middlesex, and is of similar date to the tinned food.

41. Bottle of prepared powder of Jamaica ginger

Acc. No. 1986.201.191

The typeface of the label suggests a similar date to the tinned food, and ginger is listed on the *Vesta*'s inventory of 1848–51.

42. Medicine bottles (2)

Acc. Nos. 1986.201.251 and 252

One is for cod liver oil dispensed by Savory & Moore, London, and the second (blue glass) for camphorated oil supplied by Ellis Evans, Corwen.

43. Mineral water bottles (2)

Acc. No. 1986.201.192 and 193

Two stoneware ginger beer bottles by Drew & Company, Oswestry, and Thomas & Edwards, Caernarfon, both about 1900, and an egg-shaped Hamilton patent soda water bottle, supplied by R. Ellis & Sons, Ruthin. This type of bottle was in use between 1850 and 1910.

44. Tin of chocolate

Acc. No. 1986.201.269

This is one of the tins of chocolate given by Queen Victoria in 1900 to British troops serving in the South African War. It still contains six pieces of chocolate. This could be a relic of Robert Wynn's service with the Ninth Hussars in that campaign.

45. Letter box

Acc. No. 1986.201.168

This is made of mahogany with a yew or box inlay and the posting times painted on the front. It stood on the table in the entrance hall of the main house.

46. Telephones (2)

Acc. Nos. 1986.201.172 and 173

The first is a stand type in the form of a lighthouse – a Frederick Wynn purchase no doubt – and the second is fitted with a hand generator and a typed list of telephone numbers for the Home Guard of the Second World War. The numbers include one for the observation post at Trewyn, the headland to the south of Belan. Robert Wynn was sector commander of the Home Guard, which explains its survival at Belan. The Dockyard Museum also contained an example of a home-made mortar made by the local Home Guard.

47. Wheelbarrow

Acc. No. 1986.201.171

While typical in form of a nineteenth-century gardener's barrow, this specimen is made of mahogany and is pristine. This may be a barrow from a ceremony such as cutting the first spadeful of earth to inaugurate a railway. Spencer Wynn took an interest in railways and attended a public meeting in support of a proposed railway to Pwllheli in 1847.[80] He continued to have public status in the county and he could have initiated the line between Afonwen and Caernarfon which ran through his estate and opened in 1867.

48. Jockey scales

Acc. No. 1986.201.186

This set of cast-iron scales was made by Webb, High Street, Marylebone, London, who according to the London trade directories was active from 1837 for much of the rest of the century. It is equipped with a caned mahogany seat and seventeen weights from ½ to 56 lb. They were located in 'the weighing room' in the north-east corner of the other ranks barrack block. The family and friends would be ceremonially weighed on their afternoon excursion to Belan after lunch at Glynllifon. Their weights were recorded on the walls and these date back to 1890. This was a Frederick Wynn inspiration.

49. Box of 'Bromo' lavatory paper

Acc. No. 1986.201.194

This may seem an odd choice of acquisition, but common everyday packaging of this type is rare and its bold typography dates it to the early 1900s.

6 *Models*

These models can be divided between sailing models which were stored in the boathouses and the decorative variety which were displayed in the main house. There were also half-models of the steam launches and yachts built for the family which were partly functional (to show the shape of the intended vessel) and partly decorative. Examples of the latter are covered in chapter 13 on yachts and boats. In addition, there are three working steam engine models.

The origins of these models is not entirely clear. At least one sailing model, the *Margaret Jane*, was built by Richard Roberts, the caretaker and boatman at the fort from 1891 until the 1930s. The decorative and the steam engine models were probably acquired by Frederick Wynn. Those from the main house were moved into the Dockyard Museum in 1979.

50. **Three-masted barque**

Acc. No. 1986.201.11

This is a sailor-made model of a late eighteenth-century vessel. Although crudely made, it captures the essential features of a burdensome cargo carrier of that era. The rigging and deck fittings are not detailed, although the furled sails are well carved. It has a standing figurehead of a man who straddles the sternpost. It has been repainted in recent times. Eighteenth-century sailor-made or any other kind of merchant ship models are rare survivals. Unfortunately, there is no evidence to link it to the local port of Caernarfon.

51. **HMS *Pike***

Acc. No. 1986.201.5

The stand of this hull model bears the inscription HMS *Pike*, while the stern carries the name *Aerial*. This puzzle has not been resolved because an *Aerial* has not been traced. HMS *Pike* is well documented and the model fits the dimensions and characteristics of that vessel. The model was built in the style of a Navy Board model of the simplified type introduced after 1793. HMS *Pike*, however, was not a new ship constructed at one of the Royal Dockyards. In fact, she was the American schooner *Dart* built at New Orleans in 1813 and captured the same year by the Royal Navy during the Anglo-

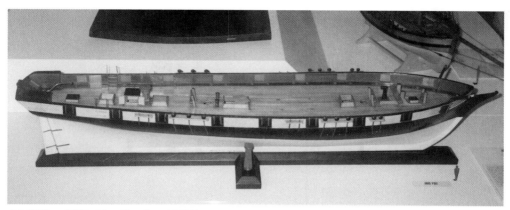

HMS Pike, *1813, 'Navy Board' model (51).*

American Naval War (the 'War of 1812'). She was taken into naval service and renamed and rated as a sloop. Her dimensions were 98 feet (29.9 m) length of gun deck, 78 feet 7 inches (23.9 m) length of keel, by 24 feet 8 inches (7.5 m) beam and 10 feet 6 inches (3.2 m) depth of hold. These fit the dimensions of the model at a scale of ¼ inch = 1 foot (1:48). She was armed with twelve twelve pounder carronades and two six pounders.

Between 1814 and 1817 HMS *Pike* was based at Newfoundland, followed by a transfer to Cork which lasted until 1830. She was wrecked on Bass Rock Key off Jamaica on 5 February 1835. Her commander, a Lieutenant Brooking, and her mate were court-martialled, dismissed from the service and imprisoned in the Marshalsea for three months. This was because they not only lost the ship, but they conspired to conceal evidence of their incompetence by tearing out a page of the ship's log.[81]

52. Schooner yacht

Acc. No. 1986.201.9

The fine lined hull model in a case is probably to a scale of ⅛ inch = 1 foot (1:96). It represents an unknown two-masted yacht typical of the 1840s and 1850s, with its raking 'Aberdeen' bow, graceful counter stern and raked masts. It cannot be linked with any of the family's yachts. John Grantham on 30 August 1848, the designer of the *Vesta*, did mention he would be sending Spencer Wynn two models.[82] One rigged model of the *Vesta* remains with the family. While this is of similar style, it does not show any of the essential features, such as the propeller and funnel, and it also has finer lines than the *Vesta* as built.

53. Paddle steamer *Helena*

Acc. No. 1986.27

A sailor-made model which crudely represents a paddle steamer rigged as a brigantine of the mid-nineteenth century. It could be a Richard Roberts creation and the name may originate from a member of the family. It cannot be traced to a particular vessel, although it could be modelled on the paddle steamers that plied between Liverpool and the Menai Straits. The first was the *Albion* which was first placed on a Liverpool to Bangor summer service in 1822.

54. Femborings (3)

Acc. Nos. 1986.201.15–17

These three models are sailor-made or perhaps fisherman-made models of a characteristic north Norwegian nineteenth-century type of fishing boat. It was double-ended clinker-built, with a single square sail and a raised cabin aft. Although not to scale (the originals were longer) they give a good impression of the appearance of these descendants of the Viking ships. It is probable that they were purchased on the *Mira*'s cruise to Bergen in 1892. They appear to be a unique survival because correspondence with Norwegian maritime historians has not uncovered any other examples.

55. Chinese junk

Acc. No. 1986.201.2

Perhaps more a model sold to tourists than a sailor-made model, it shows the main features of this Chinese design with square bows, high flat stern and three lug sails. It could be a souvenir of the fifth Lord Newborough's time in the Far East in the Merchant Navy.

56. Lifeboat

Acc. No. 1986.201.10

This is also sailor-made and perhaps represents the boat stationed at Llanddwyn from 1840. The full-size original was propelled by oars and two lugsails, whereas this has a single gaffsail. It could be another Roberts model (see no. 53) and it could have been sailed, though not very well.

57. Sailing topsail schooner, *Sultana of Tŷ Coch*

Acc. No. 1986.201.25

This splendid model appears to have been modelled on the fast trading schooners of the mid-nineteenth century. She is rigged with steeply raked

Sailing topsail schooner model Sultana of Tŷ Coch, *mid-nineteenth century (57).*

masts and carries topsail, topgallant and royal sails on her foremast. She is carvel built and fitted with a lead keel for stability. The sails appear to be later replacements. Unfortunately, her name cannot be linked to any locally owned schooners, although Tŷ Coch is part of the Caernarfon shore area where ships were built in the nineteenth century.

58. Sailing topsail schooner

Acc. No. 1986.201.26

This is of similar design and date to the *Sultana*. She does not carry a royal sail and her hull is clinker not carvel built.

59. Sailing schooner yachts (2)

Acc. Nos. 1986.201.21 and 14

These two are fore and aft rigged and have a yacht-like appearance compared with the two topsail schooners. The first is called *Mildred*, not a family name. Both date from the late nineteenth century.

60. Sailing schooner yacht *Margaret Jane*

Acc. No. 1986.201.28

This was built by Richard Roberts in 1932 for Pamela Wynn. This is recorded on a brass plaque on the model's launching trolley.

61. Sailing yachts – sloops (2)

Acc. Nos. 1986.201.3 and 4

This pair is modelled on twentieth-century racing yachts. The *Shamrock* is perhaps named after the America's Cup challengers commissioned by Sir Thomas Lipton and is Bermuda rigged with a bowsprit. She has a solid hull.

The *Gwendoline* is also Bermuda rigged with a plank-on-frame hull and a cut away forefoot and transom stern. These features suggest a later date, perhaps 1920s or 1930s.

The exhibition at the Merseyside Maritime Museum, left to right: Firefly II*'s wheel (157), ice box (38), ventilators (157), otter boards (140), buoy (65) and ship's blocks (82);* Firefly II*'s cork-filled canvas cushions hang above the buoy (157).*

62. Steam engine models (3)

Acc. Nos. 1986.201.30, 29 and 232

These three are diverse in design and date, and probably all originate from Frederick Wynn's fascination for steam machinery.

The first is a vertical single-cylinder model with a flywheel and a take-off for a belt-driven piece of machinery such as a small lathe. Its size almost puts it beyond the model category. In terms of design it is similar to larger stationary engines in use in small workshops or on civil engineering projects from the 1830s to the 1850s. The second is of an older design – the beam engine. It is constructed in brass with a copper vertical boiler. It is fired by a spirit burner which is missing. According to a label it was manufactured by Schaffer & Budenberg Ltd., No. 2836632, and is very similar to a late nineteenth-century model offered for sale as lot 442 at Sotheby's Chester sale, 15 June 1989. Family lore links it with the pumping engine at Pen-y-groes waterworks. The third is a two-cylinder steam-boat engine with inclined boiler and manufactured by the Clyde Model Dockyard, Glasgow, probably early in the twentieth century.

7 The Dockyard and Associated Equipment

The dockyard consists of a tidal dock 210 feet (64 m) long and 42 feet (12.8 m) wide, with boat sheds and workshops on each side and at the end. It was perhaps part of the plan of the fort built between 1824 and 1827 or possibly according to the W. Thomas plan (referred to in chapter 2) as late as the 1840s. On the north side of the dock was a chain-burning furnace and two large stone boat sheds with slate roofs and semi-circular cast-iron window frames. The longer of the two (No. 8) was used as an oar store and for boat repairs. It had a railway track from the eastern end to the davits on the side of the dock for handling boats. The steam launch *Birdie* was laid up in this shed and had its own pair of carriages for being moved. It also contained the engines from the paddle steamer *Firefly II* with her paddles lying on the quay to the east. The stern carving from the *Jane* was slung from one of the tie beams. It was one of two sheds converted into a museum in 1977.

The second museum building was No. 3 Boat Shed on the south side. This housed the engines from the paddle steamer *Firefly I*, the tenders of *Firefly II*, the 'Green Boat' and several other open boats, the cannon and Sir Ralph Payne-Gallwey's gun punt and replica of a Roman *ballista* catapult. The southern range also included Dock Cottage (Richard Roberts's residence) and workshops including a forge, a carpenter's shop and a slipway. At the head of the dock there was a small wrought-iron hand crane and at the entrance a larger hand crane with a wooden jib. In the time of the *Vesta* there was also a masting sheers on the north quay for taking out her masts before laying up. There were also store sheds at the head of the dock which were converted in later times into holiday accommodation and known as 'the Boys' Quarters'.

To the north of the dock's entrance there was a jetty at which small boats could land at all states of the tide and in deeper water there were moorings which were maintained by the dockyard staff. These were used by the larger vessels in the summer. Frederick Wynn maintained five day sailing boats, the steam launch *Birdie* and the paddle yacht *Firefly II*, as well as his ocean-going yachts *Mira* and *Mora*. The latter were laid up at Cowes but their predecessor the *Vesta* was laid up in the dock. Two photographs of about 1850–5 show she was carefully laid up according to naval practice with the masts taken ashore and a temporary roof built over her main deck. She was berthed on a timber

The dock at Belan Fort, 1953, with boat houses and davits to right, slipway and forge to right. (Crown copyright: RCAHMW)

'grid iron' and carefully boomed off from the sides of the dock, tied up with her own cable and other chain and her propeller removed. In the twentieth century, motor launches such as the *Lily of Laguna* replaced steam boats.

Frederick Wynn wrote letters to boatbuilders about the possibilities of converting the *Birdie* to motor or building a new boat. But he did not commit himself in the end. Shortly after his death his *Firefly II* was converted to a twin-screw motor yacht at Belan, which explains why her engines survived. Her successor, a converted motor gunboat *Firefly III*, was also based at the dockyard until 1962.

In later years there was a speedboat for water-skiing. From 1891, the whole complex was controlled by Richard Roberts, a stern man, who lived all year round in Dock Cottage. He was a widower of long standing and his only daughter, Nellie, looked after him. Her only release from the fort was a Sunday walk to church, a five-mile round trip. She remained a loyal servant and resident caretaker at Belan up to the 1970s (after her father's death). Richard Roberts was expected to appear in uniform on Frederick Wynn's visits, and in later years was subject to the latter's whims. The late Michael Wynn recalled that, after lunch at Glynllifon, Frederick would ask his guests what they would like to do during the afternoon and quite often everyone wanted to go for a sail from Belan. Roberts would be telephoned and told to rig the five boats and bring them to the jetty. But by the time Frederick had arrived, he had quite forgotten about his previous orders and took the

Richard Roberts, the boatman caretaker of Belan Fort, with Charles Henry Wynn trawling in a motor boat, in 1932.

unfortunate Roberts to task for taking the boats off the moorings without instructions.[83] Frederick Wynn also started the custom of the 'Ladies' gig'. If he felt bothered by the chatter of his lady guests after lunch, they were instructed to go for a row in this gig. This section is confined to objects directly linked to the work at the dockyard. There are separate sections on the many items of ship's and boat's equipment that were stored in its buildings. Any object that can be definitely linked to a specific boat or yacht is covered under the entry for that vessel.

63. Coaling buckets (2)

Acc. Nos. 1986.201.200.1–2

Coaling ships and steam boats was carried out at Belan and the Newborough Collection has many references to shipments of coal. The buckets are cooper-made, hold about a hundredweight and have tilting handles for tipping. They were probably used with one of the dockyard hand cranes.

64. Mooring equipment (5)

Acc. Nos. 1986.201.73, 76, 75.1–3

There were sixteen moorings off the dockyard – twelve deep-water and four drying in 1986.[84] Their chains, of which there is a sample in the collection, were hauled out using a wooden davit lashed over the stern of a boat (usually the 'green boat'). This davit was a similar design to those fitted on naval launches for laying out anchors. Once ashore they were taken to the chain-burning furnace. The accumulated marine growth was burnt off and the chains were dipped into a cauldron of boiling tar. According to family research, this and a similar one at the old Naval Dockyard at Antigua, are the only two surviving examples of this type of furnace. Two pairs of tongs, a hook and a rake for tending the furnace are also in the collection.

Another section of the display at the Merseyside Maritime Museum, left to right: casting patterns for round shot (7), otter trawl net (138), lobster pot below (141), upper Dee coracle (160), Dollond telescope (119) in front, jockey scales (48), ramrod (3) and coaling bucket (63) behind, 'flying fish' (142) above telescope.

65.　Buoys (3)

Acc. Nos. 1986.201.196, 197.1–2

Cooper-made buoys were in common use both for moorings and as markers until the end of the nineteenth century. For example, some could be found in the tiny Norfolk port of Blakeney.[85] There is also a conical cooper-made buoy from the Upper Mersey Estuary Commission which dates from after 1876 in the Merseyside Maritime Museum's main collection. The two grey-painted buoys have straight ends like a barrel and iron loops for shackling on the mooring chain and receiving a line from a boat. The third is conical and painted in red and white stripes. The grooved ends suggest it was tethered with a rope cable, which makes it older than the other two. It probably marked the deep-water approach to the dockyard. This was an unofficial marker and is not mentioned in the Admiralty Pilot Book. The official buoyage authority for the entrance and the Straits was the Caernarvon Harbour Trust.

66.　Callipers (3)

Acc. Nos. 1986.201.195.1–3

These callipers are home-made from sheet metal and are of three different sizes, all with semi-circular, in-curved arms. They are similar in size and design to those used by a wheelwright when turning a wheel hub.[86] Their probable use at the dockyard was to check the diameter of wooden spars under construction.

67.　Iron stamp 'Lord Newborough'

Acc. No. 1986.201.233

It was essential that portable items belonging to the estate were marked. The management of the estate encompassed not only the management of the land, but all the services for the upkeep of the buildings and in this case the fort and dockyard.

68.　Notices (6)

Acc. Nos. 1986.201.179.1, 177, 271, 185.1–3

The first three date from the mid-nineteenth century. The first is a metal sign warning: 'Take Notice that nothing is to be placed upon or within one foot of the store.' It is not clear what was endangered – perhaps it was gunpowder. The second is a printed sheet mounted on a wooden panel, the Royal Humane Society's instructions 'to restore the apparently drowned', printed by 'Rees & Evans, Head Office (Caernarvon)'. The third is also a printed sheet mounted on a wooden panel, detailing the virtues of Llangennech Steam Coal without smoke. Llangennech coal was apparently used by Queen Victoria's yacht and the typeface suggests a date around 1850, which ties in with the initial boiler problems of the *Vesta*. This in turn explains why it was kept. South Welsh coal had a worldwide reputation for being the best steam-raising coal and millions of tons were extracted and exported. Llangennech lies midway between Swansea and Llanelli. The remaining three are all painted by the same hand on hardboard. Two are notices probably for the Boys' Quarters about the rules for children holidaying and the third recalls a family Christmas at the fort. They probably date from the 1960s.

69. Brazier

Acc. No. 1986.201.113

This home-made sheet-iron brazier standing on three legs appears to be rather small and unstable for heating pitch. Perhaps it was a portable warming device for persons working on the boats in winter.

70. Bollards

Acc. No. 1978.201.235

This pair of bollards is made of cast iron with loose domed tops and mounted on circular bases. The latter look too shallow to be sunk into the ground to be an effective anchor against the strain of ropes and their exact purpose is a mystery.

8 Boat and Ship Equipment and Fittings Not Linked to Specific Craft

The dockyard was used for all routine maintenance. Only big or difficult work was sent to boatbuilders at Caernarfon or Bangor. As a result there was an accumulation of discarded equipment and spare parts. A large proportion can be linked to the *Vesta* which was laid up 'in ordinary' with all her spars and rigging sent ashore.

71. Propellers and shafts (3)

Acc. Nos. 1986.201.110, 111, 241

The first item is a propeller shaft with a folding two-bladed propeller from a motor boat used on the lake at Rug. The second is a pair of bronze propeller blades from a controllable pitch propeller and the third is a propeller shaft and boss for another small motor boat minus the blades.

72. Boarding ladder

Acc. No. 1986.201.244

This may have been used for the *Birdie*. It has hooks for fixing over the gunwale, curved sides and three steps. It was displayed in the Dockyard Museum until 1986.

73. Fenders (3)

Acc. Nos. 1986.201.208.1–3

The first is a black-painted canvas 'sausage' for fendering a boat while it is being lowered from its davits. The second and third are white-painted canvas over a sennit core for use by small boats when afloat.

74. Spars (3)

Acc. No. 1986.201.86

These gaffs probably came from the smaller day sailing boats kept at the dockyard.

Belan Fort dockyard, No. 3 Boat Shed, 1953, left to right: round shot (7) and cannon (1), above left brass stanchions (91) and carved tiller (76) with model sailing yachts (59), tell-tale compass (110) on beam, No. 2 and No. 1 tenders from Firefly II *(157), engines and paddles of* Firefly I *(154) and sailing yacht model* Shamrock *(61). (Crown copyright: RCAHMW)*

75. Sails (4)

Acc. Nos. 1986.201.66 and 67

These comprise a hand-sewn canvas spritsail, a cotton duck gaffsail on an improvised bamboo cane gaff with cane mast hoops, and two lugsails, one standing, made of canvas and one loose-footed in cotton duck.

76. Tillers (10)

Acc. Nos. 1986.201.78.1–10

It is unclear whether there were ten boats each with its own tiller. Nine tillers were displayed strung together in the Dockyard Museum. The first is worth noting because it terminates in a finely carved clenched hand.

77. Yokes (4)

Acc. Nos. 1986.201.79.1–4

These were used for steering the rowing boats with two tiller lines, and were displayed in the Dockyard Museum.

78. Oars (5) and rowlocks (5)

Acc. Nos. 1986.201.71.1–5, 77.1–5

These do not come from specific boats and all are of different sizes, except for a larger pair 12½ inches (318 mm) long. The latter are hand forged and appear to be of a size for sweeps on a larger vessel. Perhaps they were part of the outfit of the yacht *Sapphire*.

79. Gratings (4)

Acc. Nos. 1986.201.236.1–4

These are of different sizes and do not fit any of the boats in the collection. They were displayed in the Dockyard Museum opposite the *Firefly II*'s engine.

80. Deadeyes (7)

Acc. Nos. 1986.201.52, 53

Deadeyes, so called because of their resemblance to a skull, are sheaveless blocks used in pairs with rope lanyards to tension the shrouds (the standing rigging) of the masts. The lack of wear suggests they may have been spares for the *Vesta*. The later large yachts were rigged with bottle screws and in any case were maintained at Cowes.

81. Bullseyes (4)

Acc. Nos. 1986.201.65.1–4

These were made from lignum vitae grooved around the outside to fit a strap and a hole through the centre. These, for example, could be fixed to the shrouds to lead running rigging to a pin rail.

82. Blocks (12)

Acc. Nos. 1986.201.54–62, 64

These pulley blocks were used to increase the mechanical advantage when manœuvring or hoisting spars. They are difficult to date but those with internal iron bindings such as the pair of treble blocks (1986.201.54.1–2) are later than the others. The largest pair of treble blocks (1986.201.60.1–2) which are fitted with a wormed and parcelled external binding are of a size to be used on the dockyard masting sheers.

83. Spider bands (2)

Acc. No. 1982.201.62

Superbly cast in brass with integral belaying pins, they are hinged to allow them to be unbolted from their masts. Their diameter and quality make it likely that they were fitted to the *Vesta*.

84. Belaying pins (68)

Acc. Nos. 1986.201.48.1–57

These are cast in brass and of similar quality and design to those on the spider bands. It is possible that they were from the *Vesta*. As a topsail schooner, she would have required about forty belaying pins to hold her running rigging.[87] One of her predecessors, the *Arvon*, had brass belaying pins on her inventory of 1828–31.

85. Anchor

Acc. No. 1986.201.74

This is of the Admiralty pattern with the wooden stock missing, and is about the size for a fishing boat or sailing coaster. The label from the Dockyard Museum stated that it was found in the sand near the fort.

86. Cable stoppers (2)

Acc. No. 1986.201.70

These two cable stoppers or 'devil's claws', with served rope strops, were used to hold an anchor chain while three turns of chain on a windlass barrel were 'fleeted' across because, as cable is hove in, the turns 'walk across' the windlass barrel and therefore have to be stopped off before the remaining cable can be hauled aboard. Their ancient appearance and size suggest that they were used on the *Vesta*.

87. Harness cask

Acc. No. 1986.201.203

A large cask with sloping sides and a hinged lid was usually kept on deck in the days of sail and used to soften salted meat for immediate use. Salt beef was nicknamed 'salt horse' because it was often hard and unsavoury and the

No. 3 Boat Shed, 1953, the opposite end, from left to right: Ralph Payne-Gallwey's catapult, unnamed clinker-built motor launch seen on p. 52, Payne-Gallwey's gun punt (164) and on right, a rowing tender, a sailing canoe and a motor boat, not in the collection. (Crown copyright: RCAHMW)

harness cask was where the 'salt horse lived'. A large salting tub for beef was on the inventory of the *Arvon*, 1828–31.

88. Chart tube

Acc. No. 1986.201.235

The chart tube was made of japanned tinplate with domed lid and 'charts' painted in gold on the side. Its construction and the style of lettering suggests it was from the *Vesta*. Six working Admiralty charts survive: No. 1464, Menai Straits 1872; top half of Admiralty Chart (number unknown), Barmouth to South Stack, *c.*1890–3; two (numbers unknown) of Liverpool Bay and Holyhead to Caernarfon, *c.*1888; No. 1825, Sheet I, Irish Channel, labelled as sold by George Wilson, 23 Sherwood Street, Piccadilly Circus, London, *c.* 1890, and No. 2011 of Holyhead Harbour, 1895 (D/WYN/6/2–7). There is also a framed world chart of the voyages of the late Captain Andreas Evans of Llandwrog in sailing ships in the late nineteenth and early twentieth centuries. It was displayed in the Dockyard Museum and is on loan to Gwynedd Record Office (D/WYN/6/8).

89. Water receiver

Acc. No. 1986.201.115

This square brass box has folding rolled brass handles, two wire handles and a detachable top, which is dished and with an oval aperture in the centre. It is similar to 'the water receiver with anti-splash ends' in the Newman & Field Catalogue No. 3215 of 1929, which was used to store the waste water from a ship's tip-up washstand.[88] It is likely that the *Vesta* and the later yachts were fitted with such devices. The family still owns a complete tip-up washstand.

90. Brass funnel and whistle

Acc. No. 1986.201.118

The funnel appears to be too small for the *Pelican* or the *Gwendoline* and the *Birdie*, of course, still has hers fitted. It is possible that it came from the steam launch *Ray* or the one photographed in the davits of the steam yacht *Mira*. There were originally two brass whistles mounted on a branched steam pipe. One is missing. It is not dissimilar to those fitted on the *Firefly II*.

91. Stanchions (29)

Acc. Nos. 1986.201.51 and 45

There are twenty-seven stanchions of wrought iron with a square section base tapering to an octagonal section and finishing in an oval eye to take a guard rope. There are also a further two which are turned in brass with ball tops. The finish of both types suggests a connection with the *Vesta*. The former are shown in the illustration of the Belan Fort exhibition (38) and the latter in that of No. 3 Boat Shed (28).

92. Axes (2)

Acc. Nos. 1986.201.40.1–2

These hand axes may be the pair listed in the inventory of the *Sapphire* or perhaps that of the *Vesta*. There is no means of telling. Axes were always kept ready in sailing vessels rigged with lanyards and deadeyes. In the case of a dismasting, the resulting tangle could be readily cleared by cutting the lanyards – something that could not be done with later wire rigging and bottle screws.

9 *Lights*

This section ranges from a candle lantern to an electric searchlight, but most come from the yachts and were used as navigation lights. There was a steady improvement in the quality of lighting between 1783 and 1836 when the flat woven wick and the circular oil burner with a cylindrical wick and glass shade (the latter known as the Argand light after its inventor) came into general use. Illuminants also changed from whale or vegetable oil to the almost universal adoption of paraffin from the 1880s.[89] Ships' navigation lights were also improved by concentrating the light beam through a dioptric lens first invented by Augustin Fresnel in 1813 and exploited to great effect by the Chance Brothers of Birmingham, established in 1824. The firm famous for its lighthouses made high-quality ships' lights as well.[90]

Steamships first carried a regular set of navigation lights from the 1840s – after a Select Committee of the House of Commons recommended the practice to avoid collisions at night. Port and starboard lights were to have red and green glasses to distinguish them and a white light on the foremast (two if the ship was over 150 feet) and a stern light. The arcs of visibility were laid down as 112½° for port and starboard and 135° for the stern. This makes it possible to judge the course of a ship at night by studying the steaming lights visible to an observer. Other light patterns were laid down for fishing craft, vessels at anchor, etc. The design of the lamps did not change much from the mid-nineteenth to the mid-twentieth century, and many large tramp steamers depended on oil lamps for navigation lights and internal illumination into the 1930s. This is evident from ship chandlers' catalogues, for example, that of Newman & Field published in Birmingham in 1929. It is difficult to attribute any of these lights to specific yachts. However, as both the *Mira* and *Mora* were too big for Belan dock, it is likely that they came from the *Sapphire*, *Vesta*, *Gwendoline*, *Pelican* or *Firefly II*.

93. Masthead lights (5)

Acc. Nos. 1986.201.89, 82, 87, 88 and 98

The masthead lights displayed a white light and needed fittings to permit them to be hoisted and lowered. The oldest (1986.201.89), made of tinplate and painted black, is a square box with a circular glass, ventilator on top and

A selection of lamps: a. tinplate masthead light possibly from Vesta (93); b. Hall's patent masthead light (93); c. Foster's sidelight (95); d. signal lamp with hinged front (96); e. lanthorn (100); f. Bartlite patent searchlight (97).

a rope strop for hoisting. The construction, patina, the shade of red paint inside and the lack of a dioptric lens, suggest that this is older than the brass and copper lights. It may come from either the *Sapphire* or the *Vesta*.

The second (1986.201.82) was made by Chance Brothers, Birmingham, in copper and brass with a dioptric lens, a cupola top and an extended brass handle.

The third and fourth (1986.201.87 and 88) were labelled as being manufactured by 'J. S. Stone & Co., manufacturers, Deptford' and are of similar construction. The latter has an additional label, 'Hall's patent storm proof, London' and a fluted top. Stone's were major competitors to Chance & Co. and at the top of the lamp market.

The fifth (1986.201.98) is of a grey painted tinplate with a dioptric lens and has its top missing, and is much inferior to the others. It does not have a maker's label.

94. Anchor light

Acc. No. 1986.201.90

Unlike masthead lights, anchor lights show an all-round white light and are hoisted on the forestay at night to indicate the vessel is at anchor. This example is circular in copper and brass with a dioptric lens made by Robinson & Co., 32 Canning Dock, Liverpool.[91]

95. Side lights (4)

Acc. Nos. 1986.201.84.1–2 and 85.1–2

These are in pairs with red and green glasses for port and starboard. The first pair (1986.201.58.1–2) is made of copper by an unknown maker, with brass labels stamped 'port' and 'starboard'.

The second pair (1986.201.85) is of similar design but with an elaborate ventilator on top made by H. Foster, Waterloo Road, Liverpool. According to the Gore's Directories for Liverpool, Foster occupied various premises on Waterloo Road between 1845 and 1867. This means that they could belong to the *Vesta*, although it seems unlikely that she would be sold in 1873 without lights unless this was a spare pair.

96. Signal lamps (3)

Acc. Nos. 1986.201.96.1–3

The first (1986.201.96.1) is in black japanned tinplate with a circular lens and an ebony handle. The second (1986.201.96.2) has an ebony handle, copper body, a semi-circular ventilator and a ring handle. On the front there is a hinged triangular shade which is lifted to make a signal. The third (1986.201.92.3) is similar to the first, but has been repainted with aluminium paint.

97. Searchlights (2)

Acc. Nos. 1986.201.91 and 99

The first (1986.201.91) is of brass, electrically illuminated and labelled 'One Mile Ray, New York 800', and possibly comes from the *Firefly II* after 1932 when she had a generator fitted. The second (1986.201.99) is also of brass with a large circular lens, a handle on top and powered by acetylene. It is labelled 'Bartlite patent'. Unfortunately, its manufacturer and its date of manufacture cannot be traced, but it is likely to have been made between 1890 and 1920.

98. Bulkhead lamps (4)

Acc. Nos. 1986.201.83.1–4

This type is used to illuminate a ship's internal spaces and they are flat and narrow to take up the minimum of space. Three (1986.201.83.1–3) are in brass with bevelled glasses on three sides. The last (1986.201.83.4) is of tinplate painted with aluminium paint with a front glass only. It is possible that these could be from the *Vesta*, with better quality brass lamps for the passenger spaces.

99. Candle lamps (2)

Acc. Nos. 1986.201.97.1–2

These tubular lamps are in gimbals and have a counter-weight at the base. Their glass shades are missing. These may be the two 'bronzed Palmer candle brackets' listed in the *Vesta's* 1848 inventory.

100. Lanthorn

Acc. No. 1986.201.95

This circular lanthorn is made of tinplate and painted red with a conical top with 'dormer' ventilators, a loop handle on top and glazed with thin sheets of horn. Illumination is supplied by a candle. It is probably early nineteenth-century, and possibly from the *Sapphire*.

101. Lanterns (4)

Acc. Nos. 1986.201.86.1–2, 96 and 100

The first two (1986.201.86.1–2) are of black japanned tinplate and oil lit by the Geara Light Co., Patent No. 811, Glasgow, 1864. They are similar to the round cargo lamp (No. 660) in the Newman and Field Catalogue of 1929 and also a pair of lanterns from an emigrant ship in the collection of the Western Australia Maritime Museum.

The third (1986.201.86.96) is octagonal made of brass with a conical top and loop handle and the fourth (1986.201.86.100) is circular in tinplate and labelled 'Halls' Patent Stormproof Lamp, London, No. 259'.

The obvious antiquity of all these lanterns (or cargo lamps) suggest they may date back to the *Vesta*'s time. However, they do not appear in either of the two surviving inventories.

102. Davy safety lamp

Acc. No. 1986.201.94

This was patented in 1815 for use in coalmines where a naked flame could cause a gas explosion. This battered example could be the 'Sir H. Davy' lamp listed in *Vesta*'s accounts of 1848–51.[92] It was later displayed in the hall of the main house.

103. Lamp glasses (4)

Acc. No. 1986.201.93

All are marked 'fireproof, annealed, made in Austria'; the first two are of different shape and their date is unknown.

10 *Navigational and Scientific Instruments and Equipment*

This section includes instruments which may have been used ashore rather than afloat, such as the two surveyor's compasses and the Dollond telescope on a tripod. For neatness these are grouped with equivalent nautical examples. There is also a miscellany of what might be termed scientific instruments and many seem to be linked to Frederick Wynn and his wide-ranging interests. The maker's dates have been taken from Clifton's *Dictionary of British Instrument Makers, 1550–1851* (London, 1995).

104. Surveyor's compasses (2)

Acc. Nos. 1986.201.120 and 121

Each of these is housed in a wooden box with a lid, with a single uncompensated needle and should probably be associated with the work of the estate. 1986.201.120 has a crude pencil version of the compass rose pasted in the lid and is marked 'R.V. Wynn, Rug, Corwen'. 1986.201.121 is similar but without the inscription. Similar examples are in the National Maritime Museum and are dated to the late eighteenth century.

105. Pocket compass

Acc. No. 1986.201.122

This pocket compass is by E. Barker & Son, London, Patent No. 12777, and is dated 1906. It has a blackened brass case, locking mechanism and magnifying glass in the cover. Again, this is a non-maritime item and the date links it with Frederick Wynn.

106. Azimuth compass

Acc. No. 1986.201.123

This Azimuth compass is gimballed in a wooden box with folding alidades, made by William Harris, 50 Holborn, London and Hamburg, who sold compasses between 1816 and 1839. The dates suggest that it was used on the *Sapphire*.

107. Boat compass

Acc. No. 1986.201.124

This compass was made by Dent of 61 Strand and 4 Royal Exchange, London, Patent No. 38874, with a binnacle cover, carrying handle and lamp. Dent flourished between 1826 and 1851. He was the inventor of the liquid card compass in 1842. His main work was making chronometers. He also held a royal appointment. His last address in 1851 was 61 The Strand and so the compass could be linked with the *Vesta*.

108. Liquid card compasses (2)

Acc. Nos. 1986.201.130 and 247

The first is by Kelvin, White & Hutton, *c.*1915. The second is a 'Sestrel' type, No. 132/47 by H. Hughes & Son, *c.*1950.

109. Dry card compasses (4)

Acc. Nos. 1986.201.126, 132, 127 and 131

The first two (1986.201.126 and 132) were made by Gray & Keen, Strand Street, Liverpool, who worked at that address from 1847 to 1855 as nautical instrument-makers and correctors of compasses on iron-built vessels. 1986.201.126 has lamps and 1986.201.132 is without lamps. They can be linked to the *Vesta* by date.

The third (1986.201.127) was by Hughes & Co., London, dates from between 1835 and 1875 and is gimballed in a wooden carrying case and two binnacle lamps. The fourth (1986.201.131) was made by J. & A. Walker, 33 Pool Lane, Liverpool. John and Alexander Walker worked there between 1823 and 1859 and afterwards at South Castle Street. It can therefore be linked to the *Sapphire* and the *Vesta*.

110. Tell-tale compass

Acc. No. 1986.201.128

This hangs from the deck head, usually in the master's cabin. It is a dry card compass by Gray and Keen, Strand Street, Canning Dock, Liverpool, and is of similar date to 1986.201.126 and 132. A tell-tale compass is listed on the *Vesta's* inventory in her deck house in 1848.

111. Aircraft compass

Acc. No. 1986.201.129

This is labelled 'Mark II, ref. 6a/1174, 3c No. 47076 with remote indicator, manufactured by Bendix Corporation, Peterborough, New Jersey, U.S.A.', and dates from the Second World War. It probably comes from the wartime bomber training base at RAF Llandwrog.

112. Binnacle cover

Acc. No. 1986.201.250

This is made of brass and does not seem to be linked to any of the existing compasses.

113. Range finder

Acc. No. 1986.201.142

This range finder (No. 345) is in a wooden case and made to Taylor & Gray's, Patent No. 1899–14, by T. Cooke & Sons, London and York in 1915. It has an instruction leaflet and two pages of notes on its use by an unknown writer from Lyewood Cottage, Ropley, Hants.

114. Octant

Acc. No. 1986.201.149

The scale and maker's name are missing from this octant. It cannot be linked with a specific ship but probably dates from the early nineteenth century. It ended up as an ornament in the entrance hall of the fort's main house.

115. Sounding lead

Acc. No. 1986.201.150

This sounding lead is stamped **XIV**, marked in fathoms and used on the *Firefly II*, but heavy usage suggests an older date. The *Vesta* carried a lead line and leads of different weights according to her 1849–51 accounts.

116. Sounding machine

Acc. No. 1986.201.143

T. Walker's patent Harpoon No. 5899, has a cable-laid strop for attaching to a line and a box with instructions including testimonials to Walker's patent taffrail log dated 28 April 1882. This was manufactured along the lines of Massey's patent and was still available in the 1929 Newall & Freeman Catalogue. An older version made by Massey was part of the *Vesta's* outfit.

*A selection of equipment linked to the
Vesta (155): a. Massey's depth
gauge; b. box of sand glasses;
c. binnacle; d. and e. Schaffer's and
Scheerboom's life preservers.*

117. Depth gauge

Acc. No. 1986.201.144

This depth gauge was made by Dobbie McInnes Ltd., Mill Dam, South Shields; 45 Bothwell Street, Glasgow; 15 London Street, London EC28, and 28 Cathcart Street, Greenock. It is numbered and dated No. A151, bt. 29.68, 4.8.1906 and is in a box with instructions and fittings including three fathom rods, a bottle of glycerine for sealing rubber rings, a block of French chalk (Norval & Sons, Bothwell Street, Glasgow) and a steel weighted tube with a hinged lid fitted with a loop for securing the sounding cable. The depth gauge's brass label reads 'Dobbie's patent depth Gauge, patent no. 25712'99 No. A151, Alex Dobbie & Sons Ltd., Glasgow, Greenock and South Shields'.

118. Hand log reel and line

Acc. No. 1986.201.152

The log chip, a triangular piece of wood, which should be attached to the end of the line to provide resistance to pay it out in the wake of the ship, is missing. The general condition and antique appearance of the reel suggest that it may date from the *Sapphire's* time because the *Vesta*, according to the 1848 and 1851 inventories, carried only a Massey patent log. On the other hand, the *Vesta* did carry a box of sand glasses, which implies that there was a hand log as well.

119. Stand telescopes (2)

Acc. Nos. 1986.201.133 and 135

The first (1986.201.133) is a 2 inch (51 mm) diameter refractor, one draw brass tube with sharkskin covering on a brass tripod, stored in a box labelled 'S. & B. Solomons, opticians to the Government, 39 Albemarle St., Piccadilly, London', and 'C. H. Wynn' is in pencil. Samuel and Benjamin Solomons worked at the Albemarle Street address between 1840 and 1875.

The second (1986.201.135) is a 4 inch (101 mm) diameter refractor with one draw and a focusing rack and pinion. It is mounted on an adjustable wooden tripod, which in turn stands on a triangular wooden base with castors. There is also a wooden box with an incomplete set of interchangeable tubes and eyepieces. It was made by Dollond of London, and this is probably George Dollond working between 1820 and 1852. The photograph of Fort Williamsburg about 1850–5 shows a similar telescope mounted on the ramparts. Later, Frederick Wynn had this telescope positioned in the watch house he built over the north gate of Belan Fort. In the words of Robert Vaughan Wynn: 'A record of what he observed will, no doubt, be handed down by word of mouth',[93] and word of mouth has it that

Belan Fort, the study of the main house, with a telescope (120) to left and white ensign pipe racks on either side of the fireplace (27). (Crown copyright: RCAHMW)

the telescope was used to observe courting couples in the sand dunes of Newborough on the opposite shore.

120. Mariner's telescopes (5)

Acc. Nos. 1986.201.134, 136–9

All five may have been used at sea before being used to decorate the entrance hall and the study of the main house of the fort. The first (1986.201.134) is a 2½ inch (64 mm) diameter refractor, with a single draw tube and turk's head ropework decoration made by Dowling, London. This is possibly W. Dowling working between 1814 and 1830 at Lincoln's Passage, London. The second (1986.201.136) is a refractor with one draw tube with a leather cover with Marryat's flag code inset. It was made by Melling & Co., Liverpool, which was probably the Edward Melling who worked at 39 South Castle Street between 1846 and 1851. The third (1986.201.137) is a 1½ inch (38 mm) diameter refractor with two draw tubes made by Watkins and Hill, Charing Cross, London, who were active between 1828 and 1845.[94]

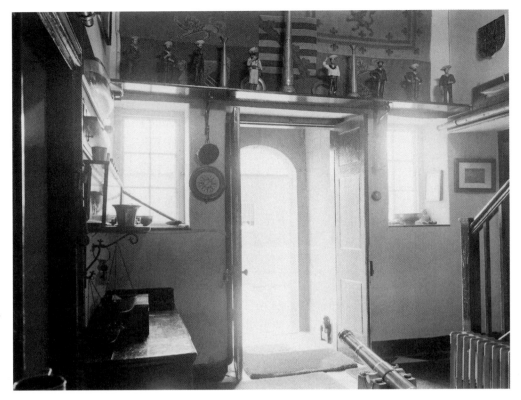

Belan Fort, the hall of the main house: model sailors (26) and speaking trumpets over the door (134); course indicator on left (123); Davy safety lamp and half-model of Gwendoline, *1879, (156) with brass cannon from* Vesta *in foreground. (Crown copyright: RCAHMW)*

The fourth (1986.201.138) is a refractor with a one draw tube in a leather carrying case with shoulder strap by Ross of London. This is probably the optician, mathematical, philosophical instrument, barometer and hydrometer maker working in London between 1830 and 1859. The final telescope (1986.201.139) is a 2½ inch (64 mm) diameter refractor with a one draw tube and a leather cover with the national and code flags inset by Dowling of London and presumably the same maker as 1986.201.134.

All five telescopes are of dates which mean they could have been purchased for use on board the *Sapphire* or the *Vesta*. The latter's 1848 and 1851 inventories list three telescopes.

121. Binoculars

Acc. No. 1986.201.141

This pair of binoculars was made by Dollond, London, in aluminium with one pair of draw tubes, rack and pinion focusing and a black leather carrying case, and is probably late nineteenth or early twentieth century.

122. Log slate

Acc. No. 1986.201.240

This is two slates in a hinged wooden frame with the regular columns of the log scratched into the surface. The master would write up the ship's log from this ephemeral record. Illegible traces of some entries are visible. The age and condition suggests it was from the *Vesta*, but it is not in either the 1848 or 1851 inventories. Newman & Field could supply slate logs in 1929!

123. Course indicator

Acc. No. 1986.201.148

This is Boyd's patent made by sole licensee and manufacturer, Delane, Dray & Co., London Bridge. It consists of a compass rose with a red indicating arrow in a turned wooden frame. The maker does not appear in Clifton. This was displayed in the entrance hall of the main house of the fort.

124. Salinometer and salinometer pots (2)

Acc. Nos. 1986.201.114.1–3

The copper pots were used to draw off a sample of boiler feed water to measure the amount of salt in it. The salinometer was a graduated glass tube with a weighted bulb at its bottom and was used in the same way as a hydrometer. It was found stored in a tin tube with a leaflet for a 'sol-horometer' – a sunshine measuring device.

125. Case of mathematical instruments

Acc. No. 1986.201.49

This is an incomplete set with five surviving items: dividers, protractor, compass with pencil, compass with bow pen and a bow pen in a wooden container, covered with sharkskin and with marbled paper in the hinged lid, inscribed '1/1/–'. A case of mathematical instruments was in the *Vesta's* 1848 inventory, but the design of case and style of instruments could make this an earlier manufacture and can be compared with the Peter Dollond set of *c.*1760 auctioned at Sotheby's on 30 May 1916, lot 142. The missing instruments probably included a sector and a scale rule.

126. Star globe

Acc. No. 1986.201.153

This is in a wooden case with a brass meridian inscribed 'Cary & Co. makers to the Admiralty, 7 Pall Mall, London, patent no. 21540', with instructions pasted into the lid. It was made after 1891 and was probably a Frederick Wynn purchase.

127. Rotaplane

Acc. No. 1986.201.153.1–7

This is Thomas's patent, an educational device to demonstrate the apparent movements of the sun and moon down the year from a specific point on earth. Electric bulbs representing the sun and the moon are missing. There is an introduction book, a photograph of a deluxe version and three letters from James W. Vickers of Finsbury Square Buildings, London EC, to the Hon. Frederick Wynn, dated 3 and 7 October, 21 November 1908, about the setting up of Rotaplane, including a blueprint with the last letter (4–7).

128. Box for self-registering thermometer

Acc. No. 1986.201.155

This is made by Negretti and Zambra, 122 Regent Street and 45 Cornhill, London. The thermometer is missing. The box contains two leaflets and two certificates of examination by the National Physical Laboratory. One is completed and numbered 151987, dated January 1911 and sent to Negretti and Zambra's works address, 38 Holborn Viaduct, London EC. This again demonstrates Frederick Wynn's interest in measuring instruments.

129. Aneroid pocket barometers (3)

Acc. Nos. 1986.201.156–8

The first is in a black metal case without a maker's name. The second has a brass case with a red leather case lined with blue velvet and was made by Webster & Co., spectacle-maker to HM Queen, 43 Dover Street, London, N. This is presumably Queen Victoria. The third is similar but by J. D. Siddall, Chester, optician, Chester, No. 109175. Neither Webster nor Siddall are listed in Clifton.

130. Morse code signalling key

Acc. No. 1986.201.159

This is made of brass on a wooden base and is undated.

Belan Fort, the hall of the main house with the study beyond, 1953. The Vesta's *bell was sited on the landing. The facing wall held two telescopes (12), the half-models of the* Firefly II *(157),* Pelican *(162) and* Mira *with a set of pewter beakers (35), miniature cannon similar to the 'signal' cannon (2) and the post box on the chest (45). (Crown copyright: RCAHMW)*

131. Pocket microscope

Acc. No. 1986.201.160

This was made by Field, optical manufacturers 1855–90, Birmingham, and is in a wooden box with three ivory slides. A microscope is listed in the 1848 inventory for the *Vesta*, but this is too late.[95]

132. Giroscope

Acc. No. 1986.201.161

This is made of brass on a stand by Harvey & Peak, 1855–95, scientific suppliers to the Royal Institution, and was probably a purchase by Frederick Wynn.

133. Sound detector

Acc. No. 1986.201.176

This was made by Siemens Brothers & Co., Ltd., London, No. 305, Mark II, 1915, and is in a wooden carrying case with a strap, containing three microphone terminals, length of wire, earphones (one set of a pair) and instructions. The earthing spikes are missing. It was intended as a trench listening device and in 1915 was in the experimental stage. It is unclear whether Frederick Wynn acquired this in 1915 or later.

134. Speaking trumpets (3)

Acc. Nos. 1986.201.105–7

The first is in brass with a draw tube, shaped mouthpiece and black painted mouth to the bell and an overall length of 34½ inches (876 mm). The second is similar but is a single piece with red painted mouth to the bell and an overall length of 19 inches (483 mm), and the third is similar without the paint in the mouth and measures 18 inches (457 mm) overall. All three decorated the entrance hall of the fort's main house, and are likely to have been used on the yachts or launches.

135. Megaphones (2)

Acc. Nos. 1986.201.198–9

The first is made of fibreboard with brass mounts and was once mounted in a stand; the second is a hand-held version in tinplate painted green. The former was used at the entrance to the dock.

136. Foghorn

Acc. No. 1986.201.108

This is made of brass with a brass reed. This is similar to one listed on page 75 of the Newman & Field catalogue of 1929.

137. Framed notices (2)

Acc. Nos. 1986.201.242–3

The first is a table for finding Greenwich or Railway Time, as well as the true time at the fort as being seventeen minutes behind Greenwich. It is signed 'H. Ardagh, major general, Royal Engineers, Glynllifon, Sept. 1899'. This was probably the same Ardagh who was a guest on the *Mira's* cruise to Norway in September 1896.[96] The second is a framed table of the semaphore code and may have been located in the watch house. The photograph of Fort Williamsburg about 1850–5 shows what appears to be semaphore equipment on top of the watch tower and it is possible that it was used to communicate between the two forts as well as for signalling to ships passing Belan.

11 *Fishing Gear*

It was common for pleasure yachts to carry fishing nets, lines and harpoons. On 2 July 1825, Richard Roberts (perhaps an ancestor of the later caretaker) was paid £2. 10s. 0d. for making a troll net for the yacht *Arvon* and the *Sapphire* carried a 24-foot beam trawl, two harpoons and four 'flying fish'.[97] There were also opportunities for fishing off the fort. In 1875 Frederick Wynn recorded himself netting 19 lb of cod on 3 August, catching mullet and shrimps the next day and cod netting again on 24 and 27 August.[98] In later years Robert Vaughan used the 40-foot motor boat for fishing. This was requisitioned as a patrol boat in the Second World War and returned for further use in 1945.[99]

138. Seine net

Acc. No. 1986.201.202

Seine nets were widely used on the rivers of the north-west, especially for salmon. One end of the net was anchored to the shore and the net was paid out over the stern of a boat rowed in a circle. Once it was paid out the fishermen would haul the net ashore. The cork floats which support the top of the net are marked 'D. Reid & Co.'

139. Beam trawl

Acc. No. 1986.201.204

The trawl net was dragged along the bottom by a moving boat. The beam kept the mouth of the bag-shaped net open. At each end there were D-shaped trawl irons.

140. Otter trawl

Acc. No. 1986.201.205

This form of trawl net has two vertical boards called otter boards to keep the mouth of the net open. The boards for this net have 'Reaper, Plymouth' branded into them. This is presumably the name of an earlier owner's boat and its home port, rather than the name of the maker.

141. Lobster pot

Acc. No. 1986.201.206

This is the circular type fashioned from withies and weighted with stones.

142. 'Flying fish'

Acc. No. 1986.201.207

This fish lure is a wooden fish-shaped board, weighted with trips of lead on its belly, which is towed through the water trailing hooks on lines attached by means of holes in its mouth, dorsal fin and tail. Its use was similar to a Welsh poaching device, the *dwrgi*, used on lakes and rivers.[100] This is probably one of the four 'flying fish' on the inventory of the yacht *Arvon*.

143. Harpoon

Acc. No. 1986.201.201

The reddish shade of the paint on the wooden shaft is similar to items in the *Vesta's* outfit, which included three harpoons as did that of the *Sapphire*.

12 *Sailors' Possessions*

144. Sea chest handle

Acc. No. 1986.201.164

Sea chest handles were a matter of pride to a seaman, his chest being his only piece of substantial property. This example is unusual because the core rope thickened by rags is covered with plaited leather rather than cordage.

145. Woollen hats (2)

Acc. Nos. 1986.201.165.1–2

These are fashioned from red woollen cloth with a black velvet band at the brim and black tassel on the crown. Examples of this type of headgear can be found depicted in the works of the Liverpool marine painters of the early to mid-nineteenth century. For example, many of the sailors in the small boats that form part of the foreground in the works of Samuel Walters (1811–82) wear this type of hat.[101] They seem to be a more practical and informal headgear compared with the universal straw boater that features in many contemporary depictions of 'Jolly Jack'.

146. Boaters (2)

Acc. Nos. 1986.201.165.3, 4 and 5

These are of an early nineteenth-century fashion which appears in many pictures of sailors of the period and are covered with tarred material for waterproofing. One carries a ribbon marked 'Belan Fort'. It is likely that these were worn by paid employees who maintained and manned the boats rather than members of the family. The photograph of Richard Roberts who had charge from 1891 shows him wearing a guernsey embroidered *Belan Fort* (D/WYN/7).

147. Straw hats (3)

Acc. Nos. 1986.201.165.6, 7, 8

These are of similar pattern to the wide-brimmed straw hats which were part of the standard Royal Naval uniform introduced in 1857. The Wynn family

The Mira's (158) crew of eighteen on her afterdeck, July 1892; the distant figure is Frederick Wynn.

would have been expected to supply their yacht crews with uniforms, not only as part of their remuneration, but also for smartness to reflect the status of their employer. Later photographs taken of the crew on the *Mira* in 1892 show the crew with naval caps rather than these less practical items of headgear.

148. Yachting cap

Acc. No. 1986.201.164.9

Yachting caps echoed late nineteenth-century naval officers' caps and would often carry a badge of their owner's yacht club. It was standard headwear for yachtsmen, both owners and paid officers during the late nineteenth and early twentieth centuries.

149. Lifejacket

Acc. No. 1986.201.162

This oiled canvas waistcoat has small bottle-type corks sewn into it and was made by London Lifesaving Co., 93 Regent Street, London, probably about 1850–60, and is likely to be for the *Vesta*, though it is not in the inventory.

150. Boat coats (3)

Acc. Nos. 1986.201.140.1, 2, 3

All three are hand-sewn from heavy blue twilled wool, canvas-lined with bone buttons; the first is short and double-breasted, the second single-breasted with a velvet collar and the third is short, double-breasted with canvas-lined button holes. It is uncertain who used these, but their heavy cloth and crude cut suggests they were for the staff. Their style suggests that they date from the mid-nineteenth century, and one of the three people in the photographs of the fort taken about 1855 wears such a garment.

13 Yachts and Boats

The first vessel recorded as being in Wynn ownership was the 17 ton schooner *Mermaid*, built at Caernarfon in 1795. She was registered at Beaumaris (before Caernarfon had its own register) in the name of the Honourable John Wynn, Thomas Wynn's heir, who was twenty-three.[102] This was certainly a pleasure craft and would have been similar to, though larger than, the schooner yacht *Peggy* of 1791, which is preserved at Castletown, Isle of Man. Cusack has shown that yachting for pleasure was more widespread around the English and Welsh coast before the establishment of the great yacht clubs of the early nineteenth century than had been realized, and the *Mermaid* is a further example.[103]

The next reference to the family's boats is from a bundle of accounts for repairs and payments for equipment between 1825 and 1831. These refer to the yachts *Arvon* and *Maria Stella* and the boats *St Davids*, *Bardsey Isle* and *Llyfon*.[104] In 1828, Thomas John Wynn bought the deep-sea cutter *Sapphire*. He was elected a member of the Royal Yacht Squadron in May of that year. The Squadron, the premier yacht club, was established in 1815 and its

The unrestored 'Green Boat' (151) bow (above) and overall view (opposite) in the Museum's conservation workshop. (Ron Davies)

membership was reserved to the well born and the wealthy. The noble and useful recreation of yachting also carried with it the elements of competition among local landed families that could be found in other areas of social life and politics. The Pagets, Bulkeleys, Pennants and, above all, Thomas Assheton-Smith of Faenol, who was the pioneer of steam yachts, all owned yachts. Local yacht clubs and regattas were another arena for social as well as sporting competition. The Beaumaris Regatta was started in 1830 mainly through the efforts of Assheton-Smith and by 1833 it included a ball as well as rowing and sailing races.[105] A Caernarfon Regatta was established in 1845 under the patronage of Spencer Wynn. This led to the establishment of the Royal Welsh Yacht Club at Caernarfon. Royal patronage helped to make yachting even more popular among the upper classes, with the

Cowes Regatta becoming part of the 'Season'. On the whole, the Wynns took more interest in cruising and pleasure sailing than racing. Their larger yachts made long cruises to the Mediterranean and the Baltic, and there were smaller boats for the Straits and their lakes at Glynllifon and Rug.

This section has been compiled in chronological order, rather than size of vessel. In some cases only a few objects, records or perhaps a model have survived.

151. The 'Green Boat': eighteenth-century pulling and sailing boat

This is the oldest boat in the collection and there is evidence for believing that she was built before 1800. Michael Wynn remembers a plate in the stern of the vessel stating that it had been repaired in 1809. This implies an earlier date of building and, given the stout character of its construction, it is possible that it dates to the time of the building of Abermenai Barracks from 1775 onwards.[106] Its early date is also confirmed by the analysis of paint samples taken from the bow area. The earliest green layer is a copper-based pigment known as 'verditer', which was in use in the eighteenth century and largely abandoned in the nineteenth century. The square roves used for fastening the planking are another pointer, as is the shape of the vessel. It is similar to the sketch plan of a boat in the Brockbank shipbuilding records held by the Lancaster Library.[107] The 'Green Boat' measures 16 feet 6 inches (5.03 m) long, with a breadth of 5 feet 10 inches (1.77 m) and a depth of 2 feet 4 inches (0.71 m). The maximum breadth is forward, which gives the typical 'cod's head, mackerel tail' design which would be correct for an eighteenth-century boat. She is fitted with four thwarts and a mast position right forward. The latter was almost certainly rigged with a spritsail, a common rig for eighteenth- and nineteenth-century boats around the north-western coasts of England and Wales. She has flat floors for good stability and load carrying, and for ease of landing on a beach. The transom stern also tends to fit this local pattern, while the bow has a distinctive rake which again tends to suggest an eighteenth-century date. This boat was used as a work boat rather than a leisure boat, and

> was still in the water until 1987 and was perfectly water-tight, providing one did not keep her out of the water when re-painting for more than 24 hours. If you did, you could almost push your finger through the planks! She did great service at Belan as we always used her for putting down or taking up the moorings of the other boats.[108]

It is possible that she may have been one of the three named boats at the fort in 1826–31: the *St Davids*, *Bardsey Isle* and *Llyfon*. The most likely is *St Davids*, the name of the fort. The *Bardsey Isle* is likely to have been for the island and the *Llyfon* for the lake at Glynllifon.

152. The *Sapphire:* cutter yacht, 1824

Acc. No. 1986.201.39.2

The *Sapphire* was purchased by Thomas John Wynn in 1828. She had been built at South Queensferry on the Firth of Forth in 1824. Her registered measurements were 69 34/94 tons, length 54 feet 4 inches (16.6 m), breadth 17 feet 6 inches (5.3 m) and the height of the main cabin was 6 feet 8 inches (2 m). She was rigged as a cutter with a running bowsprit, straight stern, square stern and was carvel built.[109] Her previous owners suggest that she was built as a yacht. She was built for James Dundas of Dundas Castle, Linlithgow, who sold her to Thomas Gittens, gentleman of Ryton of the Eleven Towns, Shropshire, in 1825. She seems to have been typical of her time in terms of hull proportions. She was equipped with the following sails: main, gaff topsail, jib headed topsail, fore, four storm jibs, 'fly-by-night', square sail and studding sail.[110] Thomas John Wynn bought her two years after he had bought the 11 41/94 ton schooner *Arvon* from the Hon. Charles Irby of Llanidan for £180.[111] Although the *Arvon* would have provided good sailing along the coast and in the Straits for a day or so, she was not big enough (especially with a cabin only 3 feet 5 inches (1066 mm) high) for long-distance cruises. Her log entry for 25 July 1826 finds her at anchor off Bardsey: 'hands employed in making tent on shore on the island and salluting guns – by the crown of the King of Bardsey'. The following year she sailed to Aberystwyth.[112] The log contains no further entries and it is not clear how much she was used after Thomas John Wynn's death in 1832.

There is the expenditure of £1 in October 1836 for salvaging her after going ashore.[113] Her register entry was closed in 1855.

The *Sapphire's* first cruise was only as far as Liverpool. The sails were brought out from Fort St Davids and provisions from Glynllifon on 2 June 1828. Thomas John Wynn and Captain Richards boarded at eleven o'clock. The anchor was hove up and sails set and by noon they were off Caernarfon. They anchored for the night and got under way at six o'clock, arrived off the North West lightship to pick up a pilot at eleven and anchored off Seacombe at quarter to two. No further incidents were recorded beyond the problem of hoisting the gig on board on 6 June at the start of the return to Belan.[114] The next cruise was to the Mediterranean in 1829 between 6 July and 31 August, where Captain Richards died at Marseilles and the mate, John Griffiths, took over. There was also a crew of six seamen, a steward and boy.[115] A cruise was made to Palma, Majorca, between September and November 1830, and after that she was probably laid up for two years. The logs resumed in 1833 under the orders of Spencer Wynn, now third baron. One item that may be a relic of these cruises is an *Atlas of the Mediterranean* (D/WYN/6–1) published at Toulon in 1794. This was displayed at the Dockyard Museum, and it is also possible it was one of the books in the study of the main house at the fort that came originally from the library at Glynllifon.

In 1835 Spencer Wynn was elected to membership of the Royal Yacht Squadron and the *Sapphire* placed on their register. Apart from the prestige of flying the White Ensign, membership proved extremely useful when dealing with customs officials and harbour authorities abroad. An account of the proceedings of the General Meeting of the Squadron at the Thatched House Tavern, London, and a list of members in 1835, are part of the Wynn Collection (D/WYN/3/1–2). Spencer Wynn sold the *Sapphire* on 13 August 1836 to Edwin Shelton of Glan William, Merioneth, and John Whitehead Greaves of Tremadoc, Caernarfonshire, merchants and co-partners in Shelton and Greaves.[116] This implies that they bought her for trading not yachting.

The only object that definitely came from the *Sapphire* is a wooden box with a sliding lid like a child's pencil box, marked in ink 'Spare glass Sapphire'. It contains two sheets of plain glass and a round piece of wood for an unknown purpose. There are, however, many objects in the collection that could have been on board because of their date and/or because similar objects are mentioned in her inventory. This includes cooking equipment, three carbines, swords and pistols, four 'flying fish', two harpoons, two signal lanterns, eight breakers for water, a log slate, a spyglass and two polished axes.[117] She also carried a gig and a jolly boat; and perhaps the former is the Ladies' gig in the collection.

The Ladies' gig (153) on display at the Merseyside Maritime Museum.

153. The Ladies' gig

Acc. No. 1986.201.20

The Ladies' gig is a distinctive pulling gig with a straight keel, good sheer and a neat transom stern. She is clinker-built of yellow pine planking, ash stern, keel and gunwales in pitch pine, frame timbers of oak, knees of maple and stern post and transom of red peroba, and measures 24 feet 5 inches (7.44 m) in overall length, by a breadth of 4 feet 9 inches (1.45 m) and a depth of 1 feet 7 inches (0.49 m). Her name originated in Frederick Wynn's time, 'a great story was told about him, in that when he found the ladies who were staying at Glynllifon talked too much, he told them to get in the gig and row!!'[118] Rowing was not considered unladylike. Lady Greville's *Gentlewoman's Book of Sports*, published in 1880, states: 'It is essential for every English girl to learn to row; twenty years ago it was not considered "comme il faut" for a lady to row but now everything is changed and it is clearly to be seen that it is the very best thing for her.'[119] Frederick Wynn was doing no more than going with the fashion of the time. However, this gig has been changed from a four- to five-oar positions, presumably to assist the ladies and at some date after Frederick Wynn inherited Glynllifon in 1889.

This raises the key question of her date of construction. Michael Wynn in his letter to the author (which has already been quoted) goes on to state that he believed the gig was very old and either from the early 1800s or the eighteenth century, and that it may have been bought 'for the crew of one of the big yachts to row in it'. This may be close to the mark. The *Arvon* had a gig but that must have been a smaller one because she was just under 30 feet in length! The *Sapphire* also had a gig and this is perhaps the original use of the Ladies' gig.[120] On the other hand, John Kearon, the Merseyside Maritime Museum's Head of Ship Conservation, carefully examined her during her conservation and found that her knees and gunwales are very similar in their detailing to the two rowing tenders built by William Roberts the Chester boatbuilder to equip the paddle steamer *Firefly II* in 1900.[121] This appears to fit with the particulars of building a gig dated 21 September 1900 at a cost of 21*s.* a foot sent to Frederick Wynn by Roberts. However, it is unclear whether this was only an estimate or whether it was built; even if it was built, it was 21 feet in overall length and not the 24 feet 5 inches of this boat.[122]

Owain Roberts in his article 'Ladies' gig or lady's gig?' in volume 19 of *Cymru a'r Môr/Maritime Wales*, points out that the north Wales regattas always had races for four-oared gigs. They were to be found at the earliest races, such as those at Beaumaris on 20 and 21 August 1833 or at Aberdovey on 19 September 1840. The latter included an amateur match between gentlemen, visitors and residents of Aberdovey in four-oared boats.[123] However, the prime regatta for rowing was Caernarfon, which had its own rowing club 'supported by the financial contributions from the nobility and the gentry'.[124] This was of course very much within the Wynns' sphere of influence and it is highly likely they would have a crew to defend the family honour in the local regatta. Indeed, Michael Wynn in his 1989 letter recalled that the Ladies' gig was last launched after several days 'taking up' for the 1937 regatta.

Roberts raises the possibility that she could be the *Lady Loisa*, named after Loisa Alice, the sister of Thomas Assheton-Smith of Faenol. She was one of three boats taken over from the Caernarfon club for races at the Pwllheli regatta on 7 September 1867. The *Lady Loisa* had been lent for the race to ensure there were three boats competing – a rule for most local regattas. In the event the *Lady Loisa*, which was manned by a scratch crew and was the least competitive boat, came last and also lost her rudder.[125] Roberts has also found a connection with Chester. Rowing was a strong sport on the Dee and amateur gentlemen came from Chester to compete at the Caernarfon regatta. In 1855, their gig the *Lady Constance*, won the Amateur Rowing Cup worth 20 guineas. With a name like Roberts, one might have thought that the famous Chester boatbuilder of that name might have come from Wales, perhaps even Caernarfon. However, his obituary in 1934 states categorically that he was born in Chester, was apprenticed as a shipwright in Birkenhead and went to sea as a ship's carpenter before setting up his boatbuilding business at Chester in 1878.[126]

Her condition on arrival at the Merseyside Maritime Museum showed that she must have had a long and active life that was prolonged by being carefully stored under cover in the Belan dockyard sheds. Whether she was the tender to the *Sapphire*, the Wynn's representative in the four-oar gig class in the local regattas, the *Lady Loisa*, or perhaps a present or purchase from Thomas Assheton-Smith, cannot be determined. That she is older than her Ladies' gig role is without doubt.

154. *Firefly I*: paddle steam launch, *c.*1836

Acc. No. 1986.201.31

The *Firefly I* was an iron-hulled five-horsepower paddle steamer called *Geber* or *Gheber* (named after a seventeenth-century Arabian alchemist) and probably built in 1836. Spencer Wynn purchased her for £150 in London from Captain Edward Light on 2 March 1837. She was berthed at Wapping where W. J.

The dockyard in about 1850–5, with Firefly I *(154). The* Vesta *is laid up naval fashion 'in ordinary' with her two masts lying on the quay. The chimney of the chain-burning furnace can be seen to the left of the* Vesta.

Sullivan 'blacked' her hull before her delivery voyage to Bristol. Captain Light took her down through the Thames and the Kennet and Avon Canal to Bristol. This took some five weeks and expenses included lockage on the Thames at £7. 10s. 0d. and on the canal at £5. 6s. 0d., payment for help to unlock and tow the boat at £5. 12s. 0d., five week's wages at £3 a week for Captain Light (plus another £6. 0s. 0d. for attendance) and the one-man crew's wage at £2. 0s. 0d. a week. At Bristol the 'steam yatch [*sic*]' was craned on to the coasting sloop *Mary* for 15s. 0d. and delivered to Caernarvon for £21. 0s. 0d.[127] One imagines that her masts, boiler, engines and paddles were separated from her hull before she was hauled on to the deck of the *Mary*. She would have travelled as deck cargo because the small hatches of sailing ships would not permit her to be stowed in the hold. Alternatively, the engines, boiler, etc., may have been stowed below and the empty hull towed astern of the *Mary*. The *Mary* successfully delivered her to Caernarfon and her Belan Fort base. Her exact dimensions have not been recorded. She does not appear in the Ship Register. This may be because she was not intended for sea-going voyages, or possibly because of her small size. The *North Wales Chronicle* of 1 September 1846, reporting on the Caernarfon and Beaumaris regattas, noted the presence of 'Lord Newborough's natty little steam boat which is worthy to be called General Tom Thumb'.[128] The report also noted the presence of Thomas Assheton-Smith's steam yacht *Fire Queen*. He also acquired another yacht called *Firefly* which had an unofficial race with the excursion steamer *Fairy* in September 1850.[129] One senses that there was a friendly rivalry on Spencer Wynn's part, who had already renamed the *Geber* the *Firefly I*. The sale of the *Sapphire* and the acquisition of the *Firefly I* had obliged him to resign from the Royal Yacht Squadron, which did not admit members owning steamers. Perhaps he felt he needed a steamer for faster travel between Belan Fort and Caernarfon when he and his family were living at the fort, while his main residence was being rebuilt after the fire of 1836.

A photograph (D/WYN/7) shows the *Firefly I* in the dock at Belan with the *Vesta* of about 1850–5. By scaling off from the man standing above her on the quayside and from her surviving engine and paddles, it is estimated that her overall length was between 22 (6.7 m) and 24 feet (7.3 m), with a beam of about 4. She had clipper bow with a bowsprit and jib-boom, two masts rigged for loose-footed gaffsails, a cylindrical locomotive type boiler with a steam-collecting dome and a steam valve control rod going to the aft cockpit, with a tall thin funnel and the engine under a wooden cover immediately forward of the boiler. There was a stokehole and bunkers at the aft end of the boiler, which was separated by a bulkhead from the aft cockpit – presumably the main passenger space – and she was steered by a long tiller. The narrow ribs visible in the cockpit suggest that she was built of iron and not wood. A second photograph of the same date of a bow view from the *Vesta* shows her in the distance and emphasizes just how tiny she was. Her fate is not known because she was not in the Ship Register. It is likely that she was broken up at the dockyard because of the survival of her engine and paddles there. Perhaps this was about 1869 when Spencer Wynn received a plan of a proposed steam launch from Albion Noyes & Co., London (D/WYN/2). This does not appear to have been built and the next known replacement was the *Gwendoline* of 1879.

The *Firefly I*'s engines and paddles were displayed separately in the south boat shed of the Dockyard Museum. The paddles are of wrought iron with eight wooden floats with a diameter of 5 feet (1.53 m). The engine is of single-cylinder oscillating type with a stroke of about 8 inches (203 mm). This is difficult to estimate without dismantling the engine. The stroke is 15 ⅜ inches (390 mm). Steam was admitted through one trunnion and there is a short rocking beam worked off an eccentric of the paddle shaft to work the air pump to exhaust through the other. The paddle shaft has a crank at its centre, which is connected to the piston rod and into a vertical guide. There is a cup lubricator on the top of the cylinder and a drain cock at the bottom. The design was common by the 1830s and based on Maudslay's patent of 1827. It was compact and enabled large cylinders to be placed low in the ship – an aid to stability. At the same time the stresses were taken entirely by the engine frame. Steam pressure was very low. The steam boat *Endeavour*, launched in 1828, worked on a boiler pressure of 3.5 pounds per square inch and 32 revolutions per minute. One of 1842 had boiler pressure of 8 pounds per square inch.[130] This is one of the few surviving marine engines from the early days of steamships. Spencer Wynn was clearly prepared to use the new steam technology for travel and in his new estate yard at Glynllifon, and the *Firefly I* led on to a larger and more innovative vessel, his yacht *Vesta* of 1848.

155. *Vesta*: screw steam yacht, 1848

Acc. Nos. 1986.201.33–5, 38.1–4, 39.1–7, 125, 112.1–2, 42, 47, 146, 147, 151, 44 (in order of mention in the text)

The *Vesta* was an iron-hulled two-masted topsail schooner with an auxiliary steam engine driving a propeller. She was an extremely modern vessel. Spencer Wynn already had experience of owning a steamer with his little *Firefly* and he had social and business links with Thomas Assheton-Smith. The latter used the wealth of his booming slate-quarrying business to experiment with steam yachts. Starting in 1829 he built a total of seven, six paddle and one screw. In 1846 Assheton-Smith contacted the leading shipbuilder and marine engineer, John Napier of Glasgow, to seek advice about a screw steamer yacht. It is clear from the letter that it was written on behalf of Spencer Wynn, and John Napier's reply must have been passed on by Assheton-Smith to Spencer Wynn, because it resides in the Newborough

A view of the Vesta *(155) from the head of the dock. She was laid up on a 'grid-iron' of timbers, with iron cables and shores to hole her place and an overall roof. Note the masting sheers behind the* Vesta. *The iron crane on the right still survives.*

archive. Assheton-Smith had asked Napier about the feasibility of a screw steam yacht 96 feet long (for tonnage measurements) fitted with a 20 to 25 horsepower engine. Napier's reply was not encouraging: 'I am afraid such a small vessel won't make a good *pleasure* yacht on account of the noise of the shaft working so close under the cabin floor. A paddle vessel 15 feet by 120 with the same power would, I think be more comfortable.'[131]

In the event, Spencer Wynn accepted the advice on increasing the size of the hull and retained screw propulsion. The *Vesta's* registered dimensions were 87 89/100 tons, length 114 feet (34.7 m), breadth 24 feet (7.3 m), depth of hold 12 feet 2 inches (3.7 m), engine room 32 feet 6 inches (9.9 m) and 'gearing room' 10 feet (3 m).[132]

The design and supervision of the *Vesta* was entrusted to John Grantham (1809–74). Grantham was the son of an engineer and surveyor who practised in Ireland. Grantham junior had witnessed his father's involvement in the building of a twin-hulled iron steamer, the *Marquis of Wellesley* of 1824. In 1830, he was apprenticed to Mather, Dixon, a Liverpool firm of engineers who were established in 1826 to build marine and stationary steam engines. In 1827, they built their first railway locomotive. The rapid expansion of railway building after the opening of the Liverpool and Manchester Railway in 1830 produced further orders for locomotives. However, by the early 1840s, the competition to build railway engines was so acute that Mather, Dixon and Grantham (by then a partner) were obliged to close the business for lack of orders, after completing seventy-seven locomotives. There were seven other local firms in the same business in 1843. Grantham, besides being a partner, was chief draughtsman.[133] Another account has him in business as Page & Grantham from 1839.[134] Whatever the precise track of his career, by 1842 he was undoubtedly a consulting engineer with a growing interest in naval architecture. The previous year he had published a widely circulated pamphlet on iron for shipbuilding.[135] This was based on his experiences of modifying the iron sailing ship *John Garrow*. He also built a screw-propelled steam boat, the *Liverpool Screw*. In 1845 and 1847 he had designed and overseen the building of two large iron screw-propelled cargo steamers: the *Antelope* of 606 tons in 1845 and the *Sarah Sands* of 1847 of 818 tons. Both vessels were fitted with oscillating engines. He adopted iron construction and the same form of engine for the *Vesta*.

The earliest surviving letter of the correspondence between Spencer Wynn and Grantham, was dated 30 September 1847. The content of the letter implies that there had been some earlier letters because it was a response to queries raised by the client. For example: 'the model was made before the drawing and therefore some slight improvements were made to the latter. These I have left in pencil to enable your lordship to make any alterations that you may suggest', a tactful approach to one's sponsor – always a useful trait in a consultant. This interesting passage also implied that the client had a detailed knowledge and interest in ship design, with his own decided views. Grantham went on to suggest, again tactfully, that the yacht would benefit from being slightly lengthened. He also adds an interesting postscript that he has been involved in estimating the repairs to the *Great Britain*. She had run ashore on the Irish coast in 1846 and, after salvage, arrived at Birkenhead on 30 August 1847.[136]

The next surviving letter is dated 31 December 1847, reporting the three tenders received for the building of the *Vesta*. These were from Cato & Miller of Liverpool at £8,460 with Fawcett & Preston engines or £8,100 with Boulton & Watt engines, Vernons & Son of Liverpool for £8,600 including £3,000 for Fawcett & Preston engines or £2,400 for Butterley Co. engines, and Tod & MacGregor for £7,180 with the name of engine builder not specified. All three had experience of building steamers and working in iron. Grantham commented that he regarded Cato & Miller as good builders and that Vernons are 'excellent and do beautiful work'. He then went on to recommend the lowest estimate because Tod & MacGregor needed the work and thought that they might reduce the price still more by including the cost of the furniture. He also thought that the yacht needed a bigger engine, 'but it was your Lordship's wish to have an engine as an auxiliary'.[137] Spencer Wynn must have accepted his outline design because Grantham's letter of 13 January 1848 included his terms for drawing up the detailed plans and specification of the yacht and the supervision of its construction. This was 2.5 per cent of the outlay plus travelling expenses for himself and his assistant when out of town. Further details on the shape of the hull had to be ironed out and on 17 January Grantham was responding to Spencer Wynn's concern about the shape of the run. The former's response implies that the latter was worried that the run was too hollow, pointing out that it had to be like that to allow for the opening for the propeller. It also noted that a model and drawing were sent to Spencer Wynn. By 7 February the hull details had been worked out and the order had been confirmed with Tod & MacGregor who intended to complete the vessel in four and a half months.[138]

Tod & MacGregor had started in business as engineers just off the Broomielaw in Glasgow in about 1834. Both were former employees of Robert Napier and in 1836 they opened a shipyard at Mavisbank on the south bank of the River Clyde. In 1847 they moved down river to a larger site on the bank of the River Kelvin, Meadowside in Partick, and the *Vesta* seems to have been one of the earliest products of their new yard. The work went quite well and the experience of building the *Vesta* stood the yard in good stead because they went on to build large screw steamers. The first of these was the first Inman liner, the 1,609 ton *City of Glasgow*. This was laid down on their account in the summer of 1849.

Grantham was clearly keeping Spencer Wynn informed not only of the progress in building, but also asking him about minor details of the kind that can annoy clients out of all proportion to their importance. For example, there were discussions on the position of the quarter badges at the stern of the vessel, the strength of the decks forward to withstand two 9 or 12 pounder cannon, the rake of the masts and the anti-fouling composition and its colour. By 19 May the vessel was framed and half plated.[139] Grantham thought the workmanship was good. The deck planking had been cut but not laid. There were more details to be settled, such as the carving of a coat of arms in the taff rail and the recommendation of a hull coating of three coats of black varnish mixed with copper oxide to produce a dark toffee colour. By 21 June all the iron work in the hull was complete.[140] The queries moved on to the design of the accommodation including the position of the companionway stairs, the colour schemes, and the recommendation that there be only one bath and not two. The next issue was the launch itself. Tod & MacGregor refused to launch her without any ballast aboard and this gave rise to discussions on the type and cost of ballast. By 21 July the date of the launching had been fixed as 28 July at 10.00 a.m. This was successful and the fitting-out proceeded.[141] The cabinet work and upholstery were substantial items at this stage and a tender was received from William Boyd of Glasgow for £635. By 2 August, Boyd was writing directly to Spencer Wynn to discuss details such as the length of the dining table or the number of patent candle lamps.[142] On the same date Grantham was discussing the crew for her. Tod & MacGregor seemed to be agreeable to towing the *Vesta* down to Greenock as a dead ship to meet the Liverpool steamer. The trials were to take place from there with Spencer Wynn on board. These began on 14 August. While she sailed well, there were a number of problems with the boiler and the engines. The water was described as being very unsettled in the boiler and steam could not be kept up with any regularity. It was also considered that the screw might be too large and was not allowing the engines to work fast enough. It would seem that most of the problems were in fact ironed out because the *Vesta* was ready to sail on 25 August, except that the 'chains' got caught round the screw.[143] On 30 August Grantham discussed some of the final bills, such as the ballast and a 'demand from Bennet Woodcroft for the patent fees of 10*s*. per horsepower or £35'.[144] He also mentioned the two models of the *Vesta*. One was to be sent immediately and the second he retained for the time being to show at the Yacht Club. This would have been the Royal Mersey Yacht Club where Grantham was a member. Grantham's later letters advise on matters of running such as the size of the boiler, its insulation and the inadvisability of long lay-ups. He was also to recruit a competent engineer. There was evidently a shortage and the rate of pay offered was not enough at first to attract a good one. Boyd's letter of 2 September also made the point that engineers had to be treated carefully: 'As it is always the custom for the engineers to be provided with bedding, Mr. MacGregor desired us to put on board mattresses and bedding for them, as they would not go to sea without it.'[145]

The plans of the *Vesta* (D/WYN/2/23–24) show she was rigged as a two-masted topsail schooner with tall funnel immediately forward of the main mast and a large deckhouse aft. This had a companion to the owner's cabins and saloon below. The crew were berthed forward of the engines and boiler. She appears to have been steered from aft, and carried two or possibly three boats (two in davits amidship and one at the stern).[146]

The first cruise started on the 2 September 1848 and was from Belan to Stornoway and on to St Kilda. The second, in June 1849, was from Belan to Liverpool and then down the Irish Sea and the English Channel and north to Denmark and Norway, returning in November. There does not seem to have been a cruise in 1850 or at least the log has not been written up, and the following year the cruise was from Belan and Liverpool to the Mediterranean.[147] Spencer Wynn was also elected a member of the Royal Victoria Yacht Club in 1850. This was established at Ryde, Isle of Wight, in 1844 with Queen Victoria as patron. It had the ambition of outshining the Royal Yacht Squadron and it was prepared to admit owners of steam yachts. While the *Vesta* sailed well, her boiler was not satisfactory. Grantham admitted as much in a paper on her design presented at the Institute of Naval Architects in 1865.[148] This problem was tackled not by Grantham but by a young marine engineer, Jeffreys Parry de Winton (1829–92), who was related to the Wynns by marriage. He trained as an engineering draughtsman at Messrs Fawcett and Preston, Liverpool. In 1854 he went into partnership with Owen Thomas (1815–66), the proprietor of the Union Foundry, Caernarfon. To begin with he lodged with his relatives and his new firm supplied two boilers to Glynllifon.[149] In 1850 while he was still at Fawcetts, he was corresponding with Spencer Wynn about the *Vesta*'s problems. The letters have not survived but his plans for a steam engine drawn in June 1850, and for a propeller dated 22 June 1852, survive in the Newborough archive.[150] It looks likely that Fawcett, Preston & Co., who were a leading firm of engineers, supplied a new boiler and a propeller. The surviving propellers will be considered in more detail after completing the history of the *Vesta*.

She was sailing again in the late summer of 1852. Between 19 and 25 August she was doing working trials in the Straits, which suggests that this was after the fitting of a new propeller and/or a boiler. A short trip to Ireland, the Isle of Man and Liverpool was then accomplished between 27 August and 5 September. After cleaning and coaling she was ready for sea, sailing at seven o'clock on 12 September with a strong NNW breeze, bound south. Calls were made at Milford Haven (13–15 September) and Penzance (16 September). She then voyaged to Falmouth and Portsmouth. On 3 October the *Vesta* sailed for Hamburg. By 5 October she was sheltering in Margate Roads with both anchors down. The weather got worse:

> 7 hard squalls, stopped engines, lay to under main trysail, cast lead 17 fathoms white sand (position unsure). 1pm. land seen South South East at 10 miles,

3pm. steam up and went clear of land, 7pm. obliged to tack North North West to clear land, 10.00pm. heavy sea washed away stern boat and all her gear. 12.00pm. tremendous high sea.

The *Vesta* ran for shelter at Lowestoft arriving on 9 October. After two days' rest and setting up the rigging, the trip to Hamburg was abandoned. She arrived back at Belan after a call at Southampton; on the last leg she had a SW wind and was making 7 to 10 knots.[151] She was then laid up for 1853 and the next cruise to the Baltic started from Belan on 21 July 1854. By 8 August she was sailing in the North Sea in light winds, all sails set, making a splendid 175 miles in twenty-four hours. She reached Copenhagen by 16 August and Stockholm on 21 August. She was bound for the Baltic to watch the Royal and French Navies attacking the Russians. Britain had declared war on Russia on 27 March 1854 to prevent Russia extending her influence over the declining Turkish Empire. A land campaign was fought in the Crimea. In the Baltic the allied fleet blockaded the Russians and tried to destroy their fortifications. The *Vesta* was one of seven yachts (mainly from the Royal Yacht Squadron) that had gone to watch 'the fun'. On 4 September at 5.00 a.m. she sailed for Bomarsund with a naval officer on board as pilot. She anchored close to HMSs *Edinburgh*, *Ajax*, *Penelope*, *Leander*, *Porcupine* and *Leopard* at 8.00 a.m. and an hour later the *Edinburgh* started the bombardment of the Russian fort that was the key to the upper Baltic. By 5.00 p.m. the fort had been pulverized and by 10.00 p.m. a strong gale was blowing and the *Vesta* and the warships ran for shelter in Ledsund Bay. While at anchor, the commander, Vice Admiral Byam Martin, called on the *Vesta* and wrote that she burned about 10 tons of coal a day and that Lord Newborough 'likes his comforts and carries a female cook and housemaid with him'.[152] The *Vesta* sailed for home on 9 September, arriving on the 24th at Hamburg where there was trouble with the crew. The first and second engineers, coal trimmer, stoker, cook, two seamen and the boy all went ashore without permission. The next day the two engineers were brought back by the police twice and the following day, Humphrey Williams, the second engineer, deserted, only to be brought back for sailing day, the 28th. The *Vesta* was finally brought into the dock on 11 October with de-rigging and de-storing taking another three days.

The year 1855 saw no cruise and her master, J. Cunningham, was kept on to maintain her. The following year there was a round-Britain cruise via Rotterdam and the Caledonian Canal lasting from 6 July to 21 October. Coal consumption seems to have been high. On 17 August twenty tons of the total of seventy were burnt in thirty hours of steaming. On 14 October, Spencer Wynn, his wife and daughter and their guests Mr and Miss Noyes, climbed Ben Nevis with the captain as valet. Perhaps Mr Noyes was one of the proprietors of Albion, Noyes & Co. of London who supplied the plan of a steam boat in 1869 (D/WYN/2).

In 1857 *Vesta* was laid up at Belan. In 1858, she made a trial trip to Kingstown (Dun Laoghaire) on 6–7 July. All was not well, because on 15 July, parts of the engine were taken out to go to the Caernarfon foundry. After two repairs the *Vesta* sailed on 7 August on a long cruise to the Mediterranean which lasted until 27 January 1859. This included boiler repairs at Malta between 27 and 31 October and engine repairs at Vigo between 16 and 20 January. This is the last year of record for her cruises. Her later logs have not survived. It is possible that after the mechanical problems Spencer Wynn lost interest in her. She was not sold until 1873. She was bought by John Whyte, shipowner of Liverpool, who removed her now obsolete engine and boiler and used her as a sailing commercial cargo carrier. She was mortgaged for a £1,000 to William Gavin Henderson, esquire, of Liverpool, and this perhaps was her purchase price. On 26 January 1875 she was reported missing without trace.[153]

Although the *Vesta* herself disappeared there are substantial relics. The plans which are signed by Grantham have already been mentioned as has his correspondence in the Newborough archive. There are also two important photographs of the *Vesta* in the dock (D/WYN/7) which show her laid up at the dock. Her bow has a finely carved trailboard and her figurehead has been boarded over. The stern view shows her equally finely decorated quarter galleries and transom. The latter has a huge carved star in the centre.

The propellers and shaft of the Vesta *(155) at the Merseyside Maritime Museum with second propeller on the quay. The shape of the latter is confirmed by a drawing in the Newborough collection at Gwynedd Record Office dated 1850.*

Her two masts lie on the quay with the mast hoops still in place. What is particularly interesting is the absence of the propeller. The figures are the same as those that appear on the gun battery and outside the fort. The figurehead in the cap, short jacket with brass buttons and cotton duck trousers has a distinct resemblance to J. P. de Winton's portrait.[154] The bearded figure who appears prominently in all of the prints is probably Spencer Wynn. As de Winton was taking a close interest in the *Vesta* and her propellers between 1850 and 1854, it is possible that the photographs were taken in 1854 when de Winton came to Caernarfon. Photography, though cumbersome, was widely practised by professional and gentleman amateurs, and if the bearded figure was not Spencer Wynn, then perhaps he was the photographer.

The two propellers and the propeller shaft (1986.201.33–5) are the most substantial objects linked with the *Vesta*. The propellers are made of cast iron and two-bladed. This would help reduce the drag caused by the propeller when the *Vesta* was sailing. They both have enlarged tips to their blades.

They are of the same pitch, 16 feet 6 inches (5.03 m) and diameter 8 feet 2 inches (2.488 m). The blades of the second are larger and fit with the drawing in the Newborough Collection showing 'Mr Sillem's shape' and with it being cast by Fawcett and Preston, Liverpool, in 1850.[155] The shaft is wrought iron and measures 15 feet (4.57 m) with a diameter of 6¼ inches (157 mm). It terminates in a flange with a cross-shape in its face. This was part of a clutch by which it was possible to uncouple the engine from the propeller. The flange is fitted with a band brake. It is not clear why the shaft was removed. There are no records of a new one being fitted. It is possible that the new owners had the propeller and shaft removed at Belan in 1873. Most items of ship's equipment survived at Belan because they had been taken off there when she was laid up.

There are four lifebuoys of two different makes. The first two (1986.201.38.1–2) are Scherboom's safety buoys made of cork wrapped in canvas. The first is painted in red and black diagonal stripes and the second in green and white. They are listed in *Vesta*'s accounts of 1849–51 as 'Eyckburn' life preservers. The second pair are made of black-painted waterproof canvas with brass inflating valve. They have the following inscription painted on them: 'John Scheffer's newly invented life preserver in case of shipwreck, No. 6 Bedford Place, Thomas St., New Kent Road'. John Scheffer was listed at 62 Wardour Street, Soho, in 1837. He does not appear before or after that date. The design and style of lettering dates these life preservers to the time of the *Vesta*, although there is a possibility they were bought for the *Sapphire*.

The box of spare glass (1986.201.39.1–7) is a box similar to that for the *Sapphire*. It contains red and green glass for the navigation lamps (1 and 2), two narrow ribbed and six broad ribbed pieces (3 and 4), one orange and four clear pieces (5 and 6) and three pieces to fit the binnacle (1986.201.26). They are wrapped in pieces of *The Times* and the *North Wales Chronicle and Advertiser* for February 1851. The box is marked 'Vesta' in ink by the same hand as that of the *Sapphire*'s box.

The compass in its binnacle (1986.201.125) was made by Preston, Fore Street, London. Clifton lists a Grant Preston working in London between 1813 and 1846, but not at Fore Street. It can be linked with the *Vesta* because the triangular spare glass pieces fit the frames of its binnacle.

The *Vesta*'s steam pressure and water gauges (1986.201.112.1) are housed in a wooden casing. Pressure is measured by a column of mercury on the left and the number of inches of water in the boiler on the right. It is linked to the *Vesta* by the twenty-four 'Eureka Gauge glasses' made by Tomey & Sons, Perth, and stored in a wooden box marked 'Vesta' (1986.201.112.2). These gauges are probably from the first boiler which was probably manufactured by Tod & MacGregor or a Scottish subcontractor; and in that context it is worth noting the Scottish origin of the glasses.

The same applies to another piece of boiler-room equipment, a water heater (1986.201.42). This is a sturdy brass box with inlets for hot water and a large brass tap with a turned handle at the front. On top there are apertures for kettles and saucepans. Two kettles survive and they have extended bases that project into the heating water below. The apparatus has a finely engraved maker's plate: 'C. MacClean, 5 Main St., Glasgow'. It is listed in the *Vesta*'s 1848 inventory.

There are quite a number of navigational instruments listed earlier in the catalogue which could match those in the *Vesta*'s inventories if more details had been provided. The box of sand glasses, sounding machine and the patent log are the only three that are specifically described. The fine mahogany box contains nine sand glasses which are used in conjunction with the log to measure the distance run (1986.201.47). The glasses are marked in the same hand as that on the *Vesta*'s spare glass box, as well as being listed in the 1848 inventory. The glasses measure from fourteen seconds to three minutes. Number 1 (and possibly 5 and 8) is by David Heron whose label survives, and he worked in 1844 at 212 Broomielaw, Glasgow. Number 4 has the label for Parkinson & Frodsham of Liverpool and 4 Change Alley, London whose business was at these addresses between 1801 and 1880. The remainder have no maker's labels.

The sounding machine (1986.201.146) was a brass instrument that employs a small screw propeller to record depths. It is clamped between two steel bars which are fixed on top of a large lead weight. The sounding machine is detached from its sinker and stored in a wooden box with instructions pasted inside. It was made by Edward Massey, patentee, No. 10 Clerkenwell Street, Clerkenwell, London, 1802. The address has been crossed out and 89 Strand written in ink. It is listed in the *Vesta*'s accounts of 1849–51.

The patent log (1986.201.147) was towed behind the *Vesta*. Its rotating 'propeller' actuated a toothed dial to show the distance run. This was more accurate than the log and sand glass. It was patented by Massey & Wyndham, 4 Birchin Lane, London, No. 4072, according to the label in its box. 'No. 89, Strand' has been inked in. The rotator is missing unfortunately. It is listed in the *Vesta*'s accounts of 1849–51. It is accompanied by an advertisement pasted on a wooden board (1986.201.151) (possibly the lid of a storage box) and it describes the good qualities of 'Massey's patent perpetual log and sounding machines, universally adopted by the Royal Navy, 4 Birchin Lane, 4 doors from Cornhill, London'.

The final items from the *Vesta* are two painted wooden panels (1986.201.44) depicting national flags, Marryat's code, the flag of the Royal Victoria Yacht Club and *Vesta*'s own. Marryat's code was widely used in the early nineteenth century from its invention in 1817, and continued to be used even after the introduction of the Commercial Code (later the

International Code) in 1857.[156] It is listed in the 1848 inventory along with a set of signal flags.

156. *Gwendoline*: steam yacht, 1879

Acc. Nos. 1986.201.8 and 244

The *Gwendoline* was a wooden single-screw steam yacht built in 1879 by Edwards at Menai Bridge. She measured 19 tons (Thames measurement), length 55 feet (16.8 m), breadth 9 feet (2.7 m), depth of hold 6 feet (1.8 m). She was owned by Charles Wynn of Rug until he sold her in 1895. She was schooner rigged and registered with the Royal Welsh Yacht Club. Her half-model (1986.201.8) is to a scale of ¼ inch to 1 foot (1:48) and shows her with a straight stern, counter stern, fine lines rising almost to a 'V'-shape amidships, with a low superstructure and a tall thin funnel amidships. The cabin accommodation below would have been fairly limited with the crew forward. The boilers and engines were amidships, and were built by de Winton's works. The engine was a twin-cylinder simple, 7 inches (178 mm) diameter and 10 inches (254 mm) stroke rated at 20 horsepower.

The only other object linked with her is a Walker harpoon log towed astern to record the distance steamed. Its box has 'Gwendoline' scratched on the lid. It is possible that some of the brass ventilators belonged to her too (1986.201.80 and 81) because they are of the correct size and not all of them could have been fitted on *Firefly II*.

157. *Pelican* (later *Sunbeam*): steam yacht, 1885

Acc. No. 1986.201.7

The *Pelican* was a wooden single-screw steam yacht built by Edwards for Frederick Wynn in 1882. She measured 36 tons gross and 31 (Thames measurement), length 68 feet (20.7 m), breadth 10 feet (3 m), depth of hold 5 feet (1.5 m). She was schooner rigged and equipped with engines and boilers by J. P. de Winton. The engine was a twin-cylinder simple, 9 inches (229 mm) diameter and 12 inches (305 mm) stroke, rated at 20 horsepower. Two letters from J. P. de Winton show how close they were and how Frederick's interest in steamers was growing. On 12 March 1883, de Winton wrote: 'My Dear Fred, I am glad you now feel comfortable about the machinery. [This was the decision to opt for a simple rather than a compound on de Winton's recommendation.] I am sure it will give every satisfaction . . .' He expected the *Pelican* to achieve 9 or 9½ knots at ¼ cut-off and 80 pounds per square inch boiler pressure. A second letter of 6 October 1883, reported a five-hour trial in the Straits when the *Pelican* achieved a maximum of 10½ knots at 100 pounds per square inch and 264 revolutions per minute. Although de Winton believed that this was about the maximum speed possible, he did

The Mira *(158) at anchor in the Clyde flying the White Ensign of the Royal Yacht Squadron, July 1892.*

suggest that a new design of propeller might help.[157] Frederick Wynn became increasingly interested in perfecting steam boats in addition to his intention to own a prestigious deep-sea yacht that could shine in the company of Sir Richard Bulkeley's 225 ton *Aphrodite* or the Assheton-Smith's 424 ton *Pandora*. The plan (D/WYN/2/25) of the *Pelican* is in the collection, is signed R. Parry Jones, 5 December 1882, and drawn to ¼ inch to 1 foot (1:48), and the half-model (1986.201.7) is also to the same scale. In 1890, the *Pelican* was renamed *Sunbeam* and sold in 1891 to Lloyd G. Hughes of Caernarfon.

158. *Mira*: steam yacht, 1891

Acc. Nos. 1986.201.63.1–3

In 1889 Frederick Wynn inherited the Glynllifon estate for his lifetime from his grandfather, Spencer Wynn, and he made every effort to enjoy his inheritance. One of his early decisions was to have a deep-sea yacht built. The result, the *Mira*, was a steel single-screw steam yacht built by D. J. Dunlop at Glasgow to the design of G. W. Watson – one of the leading yacht designers of his day. She measured 329 tons (Thames measurement), length 154 feet (47 m), breadth 21 feet 6 inches (6.6 m) and depth of hold 12 feet 6 inches (3.8 m). Her engines were triple expansion with cylinders of 14 inches (356 mm), 22 inches (559 mm) and 30 inches (762 mm) diameter by 24 inches (610 mm) stroke with a rating of 50 horsepower. Her two masts carried try sails for steadying. The *Mira* was much bigger than any of the

Frederick Wynn (centre with his back to the wheel) with guests on the Mira, *July 1892 (158).*

family's earlier vessels and the cost of her construction and running were on a much greater scale. Dixon Kemp estimated that in 1884 a 300 ton steam yacht would cost about £11,000 to build, with an annual running cost of £1,075. 18s. 0d., plus annual depreciation of £800 and insurance of £200.[158] It is not known what the estate's income was in 1891. Spencer Wynn had been able to increase it to £20,000 annually but even if it were £30,000 the cost of the *Mira* plus the cost of the new extension to Glynllifon were substantial additional burdens. It was just at the point when rural rents were decreasing and just before the introduction of increased taxation on landowners. All the same the *Mira* enabled Frederick Wynn to look his local rivals firmly in the eye.

The *Mira* was an elegant vessel and the collection contains six photographs (D/WYN/7/8–12) taken by Adamson of Rothesay, a leading maritime photographer, in July 1892. The beauty of her white-painted hull and the elegance of her passengers in their yachting costumes are very evident. They also show a crew of eighteen – five officers, three stewards, a cook and nine seamen or stokers. While the crew was usually taken on only for the summer, they nevertheless had to be paid, fed and clothed. The first voyage was from the Clyde to Belan via Douglas from 14 to 18 July, with Frederick, the Hon. C. H. Wynn of Rug, his wife and J. P. de Winton. There was another brief cruise from 20 to 25 July with Frederick, Charles and Mrs Wynn as before, Captain Thomas, two Misses de Winton, George Rayner and Mrs Gladstone (née Wynn). Her master noted how poor the anchorage at Belan was for a vessel of *Mira*'s size and in later years she was berthed at Holyhead and laid up at Cowes. For the rest of the summer and early autumn she continued to be used for short trips apart from one longer voyage to Portland. For the next two years, there were cruises around the Scottish Islands and to Cowes between July and mid-September. In 1894, she was not used and in 1895 she sailed to the Baltic, reaching Finland. The following year the cruise was to the Norwegian fjords reaching Trondheim.[159] This may be when the three sailor-made models of Norwegian fishing boats – the femborings – were purchased. There was no cruise in 1897 and she was sold to the king of Naples and renamed *Iela* in 1898.

A number of items survive from her library: a poem 'The Last Voyage' on headed notepaper 'S.Y. *Mira* R.Y.S.', a bible, Book of Common Prayer, hymn book and two leather blotters (D/WYN/4/1–7). There are also three wooden napkin rings in the shape of varnished ship's blocks minus the sleeves, with her name and the burgee of the Royal Yacht Squadron painted on them. These rings must have been made after Frederick Wynn had been elected to the Squadron in 1891.

159. *Black Swan*: canvas boat, *c.*1890

Acc. No. 1986.201.18

This portable boat is of similar construction to a coracle with a frame of thin laths covered with tarred canvas. It measures 6 feet 9 inches (2.05 m), breadth 3 feet 9 inches (1.14 m) and a depth of 1 feet 6 inches (0.45 m). Unlike a coracle

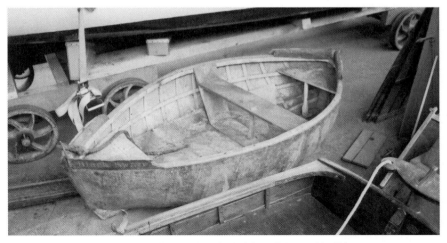

The Black Swan *(159), Frederick Wynn's boat for the lake and river at Glynllifon.*

it is double-ended. It is equipped with a single thwart for its crew of one who propelled it with a single paddle with a T-shaped handle. The style of the lettering of the name suggests that it may have been built before 1890. It was one of Frederick Wynn's special possessions and could predate his inheriting the estate. He kept it in a miniature boathouse on the River Llifon opposite the front of the main house. This stream had been enlarged and deepened to form a small lake in front of the house by the installation of a dam. Michael Wynn recalled that the boat 'was used by my great uncle on the stream in front of the house, at Glynllifon. When I was very young I was allowed to get into it, which was a great privilege.'[160] There was also a second lake at Glynllifon with its own boathouse, at the north-west corner of the park near the gatehouse at the junction of the Pwllheli and Groeslon roads.

160. Upper Dee coracle, *c.*1890–1900

Acc. No. 1986.201.19

The River Dee runs through the Rug estate and coracles of this type were used on this stretch from Llangollen to Bala. This type of coracle was a portable two-man type used for netting salmon. Their number and efficiency were a considerable source of concern to the fisheries authorities in the late nineteenth century, and from about 1870, coracle netting was discouraged. Licences were progressively withdrawn and the netting season reduced. It was made illegal to net with a coracle in 1927. They persisted as angling boats because they were handy for reaching inaccessible fishing spots. The Dee had two types. The lower Dee type, centred around Bangor and Overton, was slightly smaller and was constructed to a different pattern with narrow laths and a lot of tumblehome. This one, and its upper Dee fellows, was built with broad laths and to a different pattern.[161] It measures 5 feet long (1.52 m) with a maximum breadth of 4 feet 6 inches (1.37 m) and a depth of 1 feet 6 inches (0.45 m). It is likely that the family used it for fishing on their stretch of the Dee at Rug before it was moved to Belan. Perhaps this was at Frederick Wynn's request, for he loved old things, and this is why it has been ascribed a date after 1890.

161. *Birdie*: steam launch, 1899

Acc. No. 1986.201.1

The *Birdie* is a wooden carvel-built launch of 1899 built for Frederick Wynn by Simpson, Strickland & Co., Ltd. of Dartmouth, Devon, one of the best steam launch builders established in 1868 and at their peak in 1899.[162] She was laid down in January and delivered on 21 June 1899, and measured 30 feet (9.14 m) length, 5 feet 8 inches (1.73 m) breadth and 2 feet 8 inches (0.81 m) deep. She was originally fitted with a compound engine, Works No. 864, cylinder diameters 4½ inches (114 mm) and 9 inches (229 mm), and

The steam launch Birdie *(161) in Albert Dock, 1988, after restoration. Michael Wynn is sitting in a Panama hat just aft of the engineer. (Ron Davies)*

according to the *Yachtsman* of 6 April 1899, she was 'the first launch designed for the Welsh Coast'.[163]

Frederick Wynn already owned the steam launch *Ray* which he had built in 1889 by Roberts at Chester, which measured 40 feet (12.2 m) in length, 6 feet (1.83 m) breadth and 3 feet 6 inches (1.1 m) deep, with compound engines by Plenty & Son of Newbury, 6 inches (152 mm) and 12 inches (305 mm) diameter by 8 inches (203 mm) stroke. She seems to have been sold in 1896. He was increasingly interested in speed and the *Birdie* was always considered as a sporting boat rather than a tender. It was deemed a great honour to be invited for a trip.[164]

The *Birdie*'s compound engine and boiler were replaced in 1903 by a Simpson Strickland 'Kingdon' vertical firetube boiler and a quadruple expansion engine, Works Nos. 1000 and 866. This type of engine was fairly new at this stage and, although more complex, especially in the compact form needed for a launch, delivered more power. The layout was a tandem one, with the high-pressure and one intermediate cylinder above the two low-pressure cylinders. The 'Kingdon' engine and boiler had been patented in 1897 by Simpson Strickland.[165] The boiler was coal-fired and worked at a pressure of 175 pounds per square inch, which produced around 14 horsepower. This gave her about 12 knots maximum speed according to family tradition. She was divided into two cockpits, with the engine and boiler between them, with a steering position forward. She also had a spray canopy for rough weather. She was maintained at Belan and had her own pair of carriages for taking her out of the water. Her old engine and boiler were installed in a new steam launch (Works No. 579), 36 feet (11 m) long, 7 feet (2.1 m) beam and 4 feet (1.4 m) depth in 1903. This was completed in 1903 and shipped to Belan to be the tender of his new steam yacht *Mora*.[166]

Frederick Wynn was an enthusiast who corresponded at length with Simpson Strickland and other builders such as William White & Sons at Cowes. As early as May 1900, only a year after the delivery of the *Birdie*, he was considering another boat and a motor for the *Birdie*. Simpson Strickland were not encouraging:

> We note your suggestion that an oil engine should be fitted in the present boat. We beg to say that we think if you must have an oil engine a Daimler engine of 4 horse-power would be most suitable for this size of craft; the price of such an engine would be £210 (Two hundred and ten pounds) and we should be extremely pleased to fit it. As far as our own experience however, goes we feel sure that you would find steam generally more satisfactory.[167]

By 13 August 1901 he received from William White & Sons at Cowes a specification and estimate for a 67 foot launch. This correspondence continued and the length had increased to 77 foot the following year.[168] No order was placed and Frederick Wynn seemed to enjoy dangling tempting orders in front of builders. In the next years he was occupied with the building of the *Mora*. However, by 18 July 1906, he received a specification for a 40 foot launch from Simpson Strickland.[169] This turned into a 42 footer in 1909 and there was also a specification for a 65 foot steam launch with twin boilers or with the *Birdie*'s steam engine and proposals for converting the *Birdie* to a petrol/paraffin engine. Frederick had also asked the Kiwi Motor Works at Caernarfon to quote for a 24 horsepower engine in September 1908.[170] The last correspondence about converting her to a motor launch was with Simpson Strickland in 1915. The latter were a little impatient in replying because they were busy on war work and there was still no firm order from Frederick Wynn.[171] Nothing came of his plans to convert the *Birdie*, although it provided him with some entertainment. It is believed that Robert Wynn considered giving her a motor in the 1930s, but in the event, she was laid up for the last time in her boat shed. She remained there to be photographed in 1953 by the Royal Welsh Commission of Ancient and Historic Monuments, and was on show when Belan Fort became a tourist attraction in 1977. She was moved in 1986 to the Merseyside Maritime Museum where the Museum's boat conservators repaired her hull. This work included the replacement of the stem and stern posts. The engine and boilers were sent to Dorothea Restoration Ltd. for a complete overhaul. She was relaunched in 1988 and was steamed every summer until 1993 when continuing problems with maintaining her to a museum standard caused her second lay-up.

The Firefly II *(157), 1900, on her moorings off Belan with two of the day sailing boats, about 1925.*

162. *Firefly II*: paddle yacht, 1900

Acc. Nos. (in order of mention) 6.201.32, 117, 119.1–3, 178, 80.1–14, 81.1–12, 109, 166, 239, 36.1–2, 37.1–4, 72.1–2, 12, 13, 6

The second *Firefly* was a wooden paddle steamer built by William Roberts, at Chester in 1900, for Frederick Wynn. He intended her as a replacement for the *Sunbeam* (formerly *Pelican*) for use in the Straits and short cruises. His choice of a paddle steamer was unusual but not unique. David MacIver, MP, maintained the *Dodo*, a similar vessel, on Lake Windermere from 1881. Her main dimensions were tonnage 44 tons (Thames measurement), 79 feet 9 inches (24.3 m) overall length, 72 feet 6 inches (22 m) between perpendiculars, 11 feet (3.35 m) breadth and a draught of 3 feet 9 inches (1.1 m). Her launch was reported in the *Chester Chronicle* on 3 March 1900: she was the largest vessel built 'this side of the bridges for many years', and 'a beautiful specimen of the boatbuilder's art'. She was designed and supervised by John Rutherford, a Liverpool-based naval architect, who was probably related to Rutherfords, the boatbuilders of Birkenhead. There seems to have been some difficulty (as usual) with Frederick Wynn changing his mind. Rutherford wrote to him on 28 February 1899: 'It is too late to increase the length between perpendiculars as the said counter timbers are fitted and bolted to the stern post'.[172] Her accommodation consisted of a main cabin, stateroom, and pantry aft and crew quarters forward, fitted out by Garnett & Sons of Chester. She cost £1,193. 1*s.* 10*d.* for the hull and fittings.

William Roberts (1850–1934) enjoyed a reputation for fine boats and yachts. He set up in business at the Groves, Chester, in 1878. He started by finishing a steam launch for Thomas Dixon, a Wrexham banker, yachts for

Lord Mostyn, Sir Watkin Wynne, the duke of Westminster's pleasure steamers for excursions on the Dee and launches for the Rivers Plate and Amazon, and West Africa. He was also an official repairer to the Royal National Lifeboat Institution – always an indication of high standards of workmanship.[173] He had also, of course, supplied the *Ray* in 1890.

The engines were built by E. Timmins & Co. of Bridgewater Foundry, Delph Road, Runcorn, to a design by W. B. Cumming, consulting marine engineer, 16 Brunswick Street, Liverpool. Timmins was an old-established engineering firm going back to 1827 which built a wide range of products including colliery winding engines, compressors and machinery for chemicals and soap making. The company received an order on 8 December 1898 for a Scotch boiler rated for 200 pounds per square inch and a set of marine diagonal compound engines. The two cylinders had diameters of 9 inches (229 mm) and 18 inches (458 mm) with a stroke of 20 inches (508 mm). The diagonal position of the cylinders kept their centre of gravity low. The boiler was fitted to be worked with forced draught. The paddles were 7 feet 3 inches (2.2 m) in diameter and 3 feet 6 inches (1.1 m) in width, with eight fixed wooden floats. The designed speed was 13 knots. Steaming trials began on 26 May 1900, after which she was handed over for Frederick's enjoyment. Timmins initially supplied a fireman. This appointment was to cause problems. On 8 February 1901, E. Timmins wrote to Frederick Wynn at the Marlborough Club, London, in forthright terms:

> We are astounded with the contents of your letter of 4th. We wrote you stating what Dunbavand's wages were, but you raised no objection at the time. We have received no advantage and we have charged you exactly the money he received weekly. We had considerable difficulty in finding you a good fireman just for the season and I have no hesitation is saying that you could not have got one to stop had the wages not been good.

Another letter followed on 18 March 1901, pressing Frederick Wynn to pay up.[174]

By the late 1920s she was not considered very practical and with the sale of the *Mora* in 1920, Frederick Wynn began to consider the feasibility of converting her into a motor yacht. Cammell Laird, the Birkenhead shipbuilders, must have been short of work because they quoted for her conversion to a twin-screw motor yacht. Their plan of 14 July 1930 (D/WYN/2/18) is in the collection along with a splendid general arrangement of a steel paddle replacement. Neither was affordable but it gave the ageing Frederick something to dream about. In the event, the resourceful Robert Vaughan got Camper & Nicholsons to draw up a scheme which enabled him to carry out the conversion at Belan Dockyard with local labour. This was specified in a plan of April 1932 (D/WYN/2/22) on the basis of earlier discussions going back to 1931.

The diagonal compound paddle engines of Firefly II *(162).*

In fact, the work was started in the summer of 1932. It involved the removal of the boiler, engines and paddles, the installation of two Gardner GL2 57–80 hp. diesels and a separate generator. The accommodation was remodelled to provide crew quarters and three staterooms forward, and a new wheelhouse and short funnel were provided on deck. Unfortunately, Frederick Wynn died on 20 January 1932. If he had lived to see the 'new' *Firefly* which was finished in 1933, one hopes that he would have been pleased.[175]

Her conversion left a great many obsolete pieces of equipment. Her paddles were left on the quay and her engines (1986.201.32) were preserved in one of the boat sheds. There were also a Weir feed pump (1986.201.117), three gauges for steam pressure, vacuum and amperage (1986.201.119.1–3) and a cylinder lubricator (1986.201.178). The striking brass ventilators (1986.201.80–1) were removed except for three which were retained, only to be removed in 1939. There is a problem in assigning the ventilators entirely to the *Firefly II* because there are fourteen of them, plus four blanking off plates to replace them in rough weather. Apart from one fashioned in copper, that looks much older – the *Gwendoline* might be a possibility – they are all of a similar style of manufacture. Two small ones (1986.201.80.11 and 12) could be from a smaller launch like the *Lily of Laguna* which had a cabin.

The Firefly II *(157) as a motor yacht, about 1933. (Beken & Son, Cowes)*

The rest must have been spares for the *Firefly II* or left over from the other two steam yachts of comparable size, the *Gwendoline* and the *Pelican* (later *Sunbeam*). Twelve deck and sidelights were also removed (1986.201.81.1–12). Again, some of these may have been spares.

Robert Vaughan had some anxiety about her stability with the engine change. Camper & Nicholson's letter of 22 April 1933 was intended to reassure him and the following year he set out on a round-Britain cruise, starting from Belan on 4 July and arriving at Inverness by 16 July. On the 26th she sailed from Harwich but had to run back for shelter. She sailed on 29 July and had to put in to Dover because she was rolling heavily and 'stopping much seas'. Michael Wynn recalled that she was escorted by the Dover lifeboat because her situation was so bad. She resumed her voyage on 4 August bound for Portsmouth and Cowes. From the 9 to 24 August she was at Camper & Nicholson's yard at Gosport for repairs. She finally arrived back at Belan on 27 August.[176] According to Michael Wynn, after 1934 there was an annual cruise to Cowes week at which he raced a 6 metre yacht.

Beken & Son, the famous yacht photographers, were commissioned to photograph the *Firefly II* under way (D/WYN/7). It must have been before 1937 because she is flying the Blue Ensign (probably the Royal Welsh Yacht Club's) and in that year he was elected to membership of the Royal Yacht Squadron. His warrant to fly the White Ensign was issued on 20 May 1937 (D/WYN/1/5). In 1939 the *Firefly II* was requisitioned by the Admiralty as a harbour patrol vessel. It is likely that the remaining objects in the collection were taken ashore at Belan before she was handed over, or may have been ashore during her winter lay-up. They were a spare three-bladed bronze propeller (1986.201.109), a brass bell (1986.201.166), a ship's wheel (1986.201.239), two life buoys (1986.201.36.1–2), four life-saving canvas cork-filled cushions, two round and two square (1986.201.37.1–4), and two canvas buckets (1986.201.72.1–2). The prize items are the two tenders (1986.201.12 and 13) and her half-model (1986.201.6). These are all products of William Roberts. The model was used to gain approval of the hull shape and appearance and finally ended up on show in the entrance hall of the main residence. Camper & Nicholson used it to draw up her lines in 1931 to assess her stability if converted to a twin-screw motor yacht (D/WYN/2/20).

Tender number one (1986.201.12) measures 15 feet 2 inches (4.6 m) in length, 4 feet 5 inches (1.35 m) breadth, and 2 feet (0.61 m) depth, and number two tender measures 9 feet 4 inches (2.85 m) length, 3 feet 10 inches (1.2 m) breadth, 1 foot 7 inches (0.47 m) depth. Both are clinker built with transom sterns and the quality of workmanship is of the highest standard.

The Second World War career of the *Firefly II* began with her requisition by the Ministry of War Transport on 13 December 1939 for harbour defence patrol duty, chartered at £38. 10s. 0d. per month. In recognition of her new role she was renamed HMS *Wagtail*. HMS *Wagtail* made her first appearance in the Admiralty Red List on 25 February 1940. She was allocated to patrol duty at Birkenhead under the control of Western Approaches Command at Liverpool. On 21 August 1940 *Wagtail* suffered slight damage when she was in collision with the motor boat *Helen* (requisitioned for use as a salvage vessel). On 10 November 1940, it was noted that men of the Royal Naval Patrol Service manned her. She was still at Birkenhead on 6 April 1941 but had been reallocated to Londonderry (still part of Western Approaches Command). By 11 May, she had taken up her duties at Londonderry, her accounts being held at HMS *Ferret*. Her role embraced general patrol duties and keeping watch for the ever-present threat of mines.

On 23 December 1941 HMS *Wagtail* was compulsorily acquired by the Admiralty and continued her harbour defence patrols. These continued until 1 March 1944 when she was reclassified as an NAB (Naval Auxiliary Boat – determined by her length, which was less than 100 feet). On the same date she was renamed HMS *Ferret*, becoming the nominal depot ship to that shore establishment. HMS *Ferret* was the Londonderry base for small craft, particularly trawlers.

Released from this service on 31 March 1944, HMS *Ferret* returned to her former name of HMS *Wagtail*. She was in use as a patrol boat at Larne on 16 April 1944. Reallocated to Cardiff for 'Special Service', HMS *Wagtail* arrived at Holyhead on 23 April under the control of Plymouth Command and still classed as an NAB. She disappeared from the Admiralty Red List between 7 and 28 May 1944; on the latter date she was listed at Barry. It is not clear what her 'Special Service' entailed beyond being used as a passenger launch until 15 October, this being her final entry in the Admiralty Red List. On 3 September, her accounts had been transferred to HMS *Paris* at Plymouth.

Her final disposal is unclear because of the lack of records. However, she was listed in several Secret (Special) Military Branch Acquaints. On 18 October 1944 she is required to be laid up under 'Care and Maintenance' at Bathurst's Yard in Tewkesbury. From 10 January 1945 she was re-allocated to the War Office. However, it was noted on 30 January that this had not been done and she was being retained at Tewkesbury. SMBA 2593/19 of 2 February 1945 contained the last mention of HMS *Wagtail* when she was listed for disposal.[177] As the steam yacht *Firefly II*, she was still listed in Lloyd's *Register of Yachts* until 1949 as acquired by His Majesty's Government. However, this should not be taken as proof of her existence on this date. In all probability, Lloyd's had simply not been informed of the vessel's disposal.

Bathurst's at Tewkesbury used several small craft as run-arounds until no longer seaworthy or irreparable. Often vessels were simply left to rot at these small boatyards or were burnt after being broken up (in the case of wooden hulled boats). The Ministry of Transport's 'Small Craft Service List – Supplement 5', declares that *Firefly II* was sold back to her owner in August 1946. Michael Wynn recalled that the vessel was in such poor condition that they did not take up this offer. Her fate thus remains unknown.

163. *Mora*: steam yacht, 1904

The *Mora* was a single-screw steel steam yacht built by Lobnitz & Co., Renfrew, to the design of G. L. Watson who had designed her predecessor. She measured 202 gross tons, 135 feet 6 inches (41.3 m) length, 19 feet (5.8 m) breadth, 10 feet 9 inches (3.3 m) depth. Her engines were triple expansion, cylinder diameters 10 inches (254 mm), 16 inches (406 mm), 22 inches (559 mm), with a stroke of 22 inches (559 mm), built by Lobnitz and rated at 60 horsepower. The boiler pressure was 200 pounds per square inch. She was slightly shorter than the *Mira* but with larger superstructure. A blueprint of her general arrangement at ⅛ inch to one foot dated 11 September 1911 is part of the collection (D/WYN/2/17) and her cased half-model was displayed in the entrance hall of the main house at the fort. It is clear from the Newborough archive that Frederick Wynn was in discussion with G. L. Watson as early as 1901, and a specification agreed and tenders placed in 1902–3.[178] The *Mora* was employed in the same way as her predecessor and her expenses were similarly large. The wages bill for 1906, for example, was no less than £881. 12s. 5d.[179] In 1906, there appears to have been an attempt to offset her running costs by chartering her, but this

The steam yacht Mora *(163) in the Clyde, 1904.*

was only taken to a draft drawn up by G. L. Watson & Co.[180] In the autumn of 1910 the *Mora* was laid up at Cowes and put up for sale on 9 January 1911. The secretary of the Royal Yacht Squadron acted as her sale broker. This was part of his normal service to members of the Squadron. She was eventually sold on 2 June 1916 for £6,750 to Mr J. Withers. There was a dispute over the 5 per cent commission due to the Squadron's secretary who won his case against Frederick Wynn in the Commercial Division of King's Bench on 29 March 1917.[181] According to Lloyd's *Register of Yachts*, by 1920 she was owned by A. Axarlis, a Greek shipowner of London and of Piraeus, and renamed *Manna*.

Only a few items survive in the Wynn Collection: the ship's visitors' book, photographs and the blueprint already mentioned. The visitors' book (D/WYN/4/1) starts on 25 June 1904 with G. L. Watson and his wife. From 23 July to 7 August she was at Cowes, where visitors included Admiral Montague and Sir John and Lady Burgoyne. There were no more entries after August 1905 at Jersey until it was used on board the *Firefly II* in 1934. The photographs were taken by Stephen Cribb of Southsea, Portsmouth, which show her under way on the port side, Frederick Wynn on the forecastle with his crew and again at the stern with some lady guests (D/WYN/7). These photographs are not dated but they may be the same date as a photograph by Johnson & Logan of Portsmouth of the fleet at the Coronation Naval Review dated 24 June 1911.

Sir Ralph Payne-Gallwey and one of his gun punts at Belan with his crew, Mr C. Croutear.

Oh! Belan thou art beautiful as everybody knows.
The Straits so full of fish and fowl right past thy fortress flows
Tis not the fish nor yet the fowl that prey upon my mind
My joy would be too great for words if Ann were less unkind

R.T.P-G. Jan: 23.1905.

Sir Ralph's lament.

164. Gun punt and carriage, 1907

Acc. No. 1986.201.23, 69, 253

The large shallow Foryd Bay inlet alongside Belan Fort was an ideal place for wildfowling. Sir Ralph Payne-Gallwey (1848–1916), the Victorian authority on wildfowling, became a friend of Frederick Wynn. He was a frequent visitor with his gun punts to try his luck at Belan Fort.[182] Punt gunning involved the use of a shallow draft punt with a low freeboard which was capable of being rowed, sailed or quanted in shallow water, to stalk flocks of ducks and geese. It was equipped with a very large calibre muzzle-loading shotgun which was fired over the bow. There was great skill in manœuvring the punt within range without detection. Because the gun was a muzzle-loader, only one shot was possible. This form of wildfowling was found all around the British coast and in Ireland, and in some regions such as the Norfolk Broads, it was carried on on a professional basis to supply the demands of the London poultry markets. At the same time its high stalking skills attracted the gentleman sportsman.

This two-man punt measures 23 feet 4 inches (7.1 m) length, 3 feet 9 inches (1.2 m) breadth and was built by Pickett at West Quay, Southampton, at an unknown date for Payne-Gallwey. It came with its own horse-drawn carriage so that it could be taken some distance to a suitable launching place. Payne-Gallwey generously gave it to Frederick Wynn in 1907. The latter,

Sir Ralph setting out across Foryd Bay with the punt on its carriage (164).

though a shooting man, was probably far too timid to try and use it, according to his nephew Michael Wynn. He also left a sketch of his punt in action with this verse:

> Oh! Belan thou art beautiful everyone knows.
> The Straits so full of fish and fowl past thy fortress flows.
> Tis not the fish nor yet the fowl that prey upon my mind.
> My joy would be too great for words if Ann were less unkind.

Ann was Frederick's formidable housekeeper. Perhaps he had dirtied the floors in his muddy seaboots!

The punt is complete with its gun, ammunition box with paper cartridges, wads and shot. The gun is a muzzle-loader probably made by Holland & Holland, London (Payne-Gallwey's usual supplier) and proof-tested at Birmingham before 1904. With 6¼ ounces of powder it could discharge 2 pounds of shot. The propelling equipment includes a sail, paddles and different sizes of setting poles and hand paddles by which the craft could be moved by the wildfowler in shallow water while lying down. They had iron-shod fork-shaped ends to gain some purchase from the bottom mud or sand. There is also another paddle with iron-shod fork-shaped blade in the collection (1986.201.69) which appears to be much older than those that came with the punt (1986.201.61). It may well be that the Wynns had their own duck punt before this superb example was given to them. This is also suggested by the 'CHR. WYNN' inscription on the ammunition box and the two Newton Keates of Liverpool bags for shot dating to about the 1880s (1986.201.253). A photograph in the collection (D/WYN//7) shows Payne-Gallwey with another punt about to set out on an expedition with a Mr Croutear as crew.

Payne-Gallwey, besides his passion for shooting, took an enthusiastic interest in history and investigated the mystery of Maria Stella's birth in his book published in 1908. He was also keen on historical reconstructions long before they became the subject of television documentaries. He was fascinated by ancient archery weapons in particular, and demonstrated how effective medieval crossbows and Roman catapults could be. He shot a crossbow bolt across the Menai Straits from Belan, a total of 433 yards, on 25 November 1901. He also built a large Roman type of balista catapult between 1899 and 1903, which was capable of throwing a 5 pound stone across the Menai Straits. The balista was preserved at Belan Dockyard along with his punt. It was acquired by the Royal Armouries in 1986.

165. Sailing canoes (2), *c.*1900–1914

Acc. Nos. 1986.201.24.1 and 2

This pair measures 14 feet 4 inches (4.38 m) in length, 2 feet 7 inches (0.76 m) breadth and 11 inches (0.28 m) depth. They are clinker built and carry a short mast. According to family tradition, they were built in Japan. However, they show no characteristics of traditional Japanese boat design and indeed are very similar to the 'Rob Roy' canoe designs that were popularized in the British Isles by John 'Rob Roy' MacGregor (1825–92) from 1866 onwards, and in fact they compare very closely with the Rob Roy canoe held in the collections of the National Maritime Museum. The fifth Lord Newborough probably brought them back after one of his voyages as a Merchant Navy officer in the Far East, sometime after 1900 and before 1914.

Although the canoes were displayed at Belan, they were originally used on the lake at Rug. Michael Wynn recalled that they were extremely unstable and their frequent capsizes were the object of much merriment, particularly when it was an unwary guest who was the victim. Unfortunately, the original sails have not survived, but it is likely that these would be of a standing lug design. In fact, the unattributed sails (1986.201.66 and 67) would have been of a suitable size. Given the fact that these canoes have no centreboard, one can readily appreciate that they would be both unstable under sail and also difficult to tack.

Notes

1.   G. Roberts, 'The Glynnes and the Wynns of Glynllifon', in G. Roberts, *Aspects of Welsh History: Selected Papers of the late Glyn Roberts* (Cardiff, 1969), 160–78.
2.   A. H. Dodd, *A History of Caernarvonshire, 1289–1900* (Caernarfon, 1968), 189–191.
3.   Ibid., 195.
4.   L. Colley, *Britons, Forging the Nation, 1707–1837* (London, 1992), 88.
5.   E. A. Jones, 'The Society or Garrison at Fort Williamsburg', *Y Cymmrodor* 44 (1935), 80–103. The Book of Laws and the Enrolment and Muster Book are part of the Newborough Collection (XD2) at Gwynedd Record Office.
6.   M. Reed, *The Making of Britain: The Georgian Triumph, 1700–1830* (London, 1983), 82.
7.   *Royal Commission for Ancient Monuments, Wales and Monmouth, Caernarvonshire*, vol. 2 (London, 1960), 187–8.
8.   G. Headley, and W. Meulenkamp, *Follies: A Guide to Rogue Architecture in England, Scotland and Wales* (London, 1986), 159, 225. See also B. Jones, *Follies and Grottoes* (London, 1953), 18–19.
9.   G. Cousins, *The Defenders* (London, 1968), 216. The Royal Commission's survey report noted that weapons were still displayed in the building on 5 September 1953.
10. National Library of Wales, Glynllifon Deeds and Documents 2339 and 2371, later transferred to Gwynedd Record Office as the Newborough Collection, GRO XD/2.
11. G. Roberts, 'Glynnes and Wynns', 170.
12. Another example of noble indebtedness was the Coke family's estate at Holkham which had debts of £100,000 and annual interest payments of £4,000 in 1776 – see S. Wade Martins, *A Great Estate at Work* (Cambridge, 1980), 58.
13. J. M. Robinson, *The English Country Estate* (London, 1988), 61–2.
14. From Plas Newydd MSS II, 199, University College of North Wales, quoted in Roberts, 'Glynnes and Wynns', 170.
15. R. Payne-Gallwey, *The Mystery of Maria Stella* (London, 1908), 20–1.
16. C. Hibbert, *Florence: Biography of a City* (London, 1993), 208–19, also D. Carperetto and G. Ricuperati, *Italy in the Age of Reason, 1685–1789* (London, 1987), 311.
17. Payne-Gallwey, *Mystery*, 21–39.
18. Lord Newborough's landlord had already sued for arrears of rent in 1796 (Gwynedd Record Office XD2/4538).
19. The Newborough Collection at Gwynedd Record Office contains numerous records which show how the executors and trustees managed the debts, such as XD2/4597/4599/4600 valuation of furniture and utensils, statement of debts and schedule of creditors of about 1807. A schedule of encumbrances on the estate dating from December 1821 (XD/2/4568) showed there was still some way to go. On the other hand, there were sufficient funds for the construction of the fort, the dockyard and the mausoleum.
20. GRO XD2/4665 and 4666.
21. Payne-Gallwey, *Mystery*, and Roberts, 'Glynnes and Wynns', 173–6. The latter provides a judicious summary and there have been various later accounts which

summarize Payne-Gallwey's positive conclusions, such as Ivor Wynne Jones's account in his guide to Fort Belan of 1979.

22. P. B. Williams, *The Tourists' Guide to the County of Caernarvon* (Caernarfon, 1821), 151.

23. A. H. Dodd, *The Industrial Revolution in North Wales* (Cardiff, 1971), 79.

24. The Newboroughs and their quarries are thoroughly explored in G. Haulfryn Williams, 'Lord Newborough and Mr. Maddocks' "Very Fortunate Circumstances"', in *Industrial Gwynedd/Gwynedd Diwydiannol*, 9 (1997), 26–33.

25. *The Memoirs of Sir Llewellyn Turner*, ed. J. E. Vincent (London, 1903), 180–1.

26. *Royal Commission Caernarvonshire*, 186.

27. D. Cannadine, *The Decline and Fall of the British Aristocracy* (New Haven and London, 1990), 373.

28. *Illustrated London News* (22 October 1859), 395.

29. Roberts, 'Glynnes and Wynns', 175.

30. R. V. Wynn, *A Short History of Belan Fort and Rûg* (private publication, *c*.1950).

31. 'Lord Newborough – Master mariner', *Sea Breezes* (NS), 17 (1954), 92–5, and *Navy Lists* (1915–19).

32. Interview with Gerald Williams, published in the *Liverpool Daily Post* – undated cutting, *c*.1966–70.

33. *Liverpool Daily Post* (10 December 1985 and 13 May 1986).

34. J. Steegman, *Portraits in Welsh Houses*, vol. 1 (Cardiff, 1957).

35. GRO XD2/14229 and 14250 John Spooner's letter to Lord Newborough in London, 17 August 1802, and George Bettiss's accounts for building at Fort St Davids, 1824–7.

36. GRO XD2/9075, Miscellaneous bills, September 1836.

37. *Royal Commission Caernarvonshire*, 220.

38. GRO XD2/14229, John Spooner described the Newborough Volunteers' march from the barracks to the shore where they drank the health of and cheered the prince of Wales, Lord and Lady Newborough and their son with answering gun salutes from a cutter in the Straits.

39. GRO XD2/14250 and 1616.

40. A. Eames, *Shrouded Quays (Lost Parts of Wales)* (Llanrwst, 1991), 71.

41. GRO XD2/9033, miscellaneous bills, July 1833.

42. A. Eames, *Ships and Seamen of Anglesey* (Llangefni, 1973), 108.

43. GRO XD2/9033, 14250.

44. For example, the American commander, John Paul Jones, had caused panic in the Irish Sea in 1778, and in 1780 two postal packets sailing from Holyhead had been captured by the American privateer, *Black Prince*. G. Place, *The Rise and Fall of Parkgate, Passenger Port for Ireland, 1686–1815* (Manchester, 1994), 134.

45. Wynn, *Short History*.

46. K. McCarron, *Fort Perch Rock and the Defence of the Mersey* (Birkenhead, 1991), 18–23.

47. GRO XD/2, 14226 and 14227.

48. B. Owen, *The History of the Welsh Militia and Volunteer Corps*, vol. 1, *Anglesey and Caernarvonshire* (Caernarfon, 1989), 102–3.

49. GRO XD/2, 14229.

50. The Newborough Records contain a long correspondence about the accounts of the Volunteers which were never finally settled because those involved had been drowned.

51. Illustrated in I. Wynne Jones, *Fort Belan Official Guide* (Llanwnda, 1979), 6.

52. GRO XD/2, 14235.

53. Owen, *Welsh Militia*, 111.

54. Wynn, *Short History*.

55. Wynne Jones, *Fort Belan*, 11 and 12, and R. Chambers Jones, *Bless 'em All: Aspects of the War in North West Wales 1939–1945* (Wrexham, 1995), 62–3, 71–2.

56. Sale particulars compiled by Strutt & Parker, Leathes and Bickerton, Chester and London, 1986, 3. Note also that George Bettiss's accounts (GRO XD2/14250) include items for the repair of gun carriages (33/200) and the shipment of two long 9 pounders from Liverpool (33/189). The latter seem to have disappeared.

57. Wynn, *Short History*. The obituary of the seventh Lord Newborough in the *Daily Telegraph* (13 October 1998) states there were forty-eight guns.

58. Walthew, *From Rock and Tempest: The Life of Captain George William Manby* (London, 1971), 33–5.

59. I. Ousby, *The Englishman's England: Taste, Travel and the Rise of Tourism* (Cambridge, 1990), 150–1, 163–5.

60. *Memoirs of Turner*, ed. Vincent, 320.

61. C. C. Hendry, 'The Falkirk Cannon', in *Guns Review* (May 1983), 350–1.

62. B. Greenhill, 'The Schooner Peggy', *Journal of the Manx Museum*, 7 (1968), 68–76.

63. B. P. Hughes, *British Smooth-Bore Artillery* (London, 1969), 47–8.

64. GRO XD2/13440, and G. Clifton, *Dictionary of British Instrument Makers, 1550–1851* (London, 1995), 290–1. Please note that all subsequent dates of instrument-makers are taken from this excellent source unless otherwise stated.

65. Hughes, *Artillery*, 48.

66. GRO XD2/13440, account book of the *Vesta* with list of stores on board, 1849–51.

67. H. T. A. Bosanquet, *The Naval Officer's Sword* (London, 1955), 8, 17. W. Parker is not listed as a sword-maker by Bosanquet. Parker's account is in GRO XD2/8009.

68. Owen, *Welsh Militia*, 111.

69. *Royal Commission Caernarvonshire*, 188.

70. Owen, *Welsh Militia*, 102.

71. D. Yarwood, *English Costume* (5th edn. London, 1979), 198–200.

72. GRO XD2/4111, the *Brecon* built by R. & J. Evans, Liverpool, iron steamer of 875 tons for Richard Mills & Co., Liverpool, with compound engines and boiler manufactured by de Winton. Her successful trials in the Straits were reported in the *Caernarvon and Denbigh Herald* (27 February 1875).

73. L. Lloyd, *The Port of Caernarvon 1793–1800* (Caernarfon, 1989), 135. It was quite usual for a master to stand by the wreck of his ship to assist with the salvage of the cargo and any saleable equipment. Another example was the wreck of the American ship *Franchise* in 1855 with cotton and rosin from Charleston for Liverpool. See M. K. Stammers, 'The Wreck of the Franchise', *Maritime Wales*, 11 (1987), 97–100.

74. Captain R. P. Williamson's diary, Harrison Line newsletter (1993), 73. The wreck was also reported in the *Caernarvon and Denbigh Herald* on 18 January 1845.

75. Lloyd, *Port of Caernarvon*, 135–6.

76. Yarwood, *English Costume*, 200–2.

77. *Vesta's* inventory for probably 1848 and accounts for 1849–51, GRO XD2/13437 and 13440, and *Sapphire* XD2/13380. There is also a list of furniture, fittings and sundries put on board by William Boyd & Son, 15 St Enoch Street, Glasgow, dated 26 August 1848, when they fitted out the *Vesta* for her maiden voyage, GRO XD2/9194.

78. GRO XD2/9194, 'one dozen black tin shaving mugs at 1/6 each', the same list also lists a Britannia metal soup ladle and a sugar bowl.

79. *International Tin Research and Development Council Report*, 85 (Greenford, Middlesex, 1939), 22–33.

80. Lloyd, *Port of Caernarvon*, 261.

81. Public Record Office, Adm. 1/5482.

82. GRO XD2/13423, John Grantham, Liverpool to Lord Newborough, 30 August 1848.

83. Interview with Michael Wynn, the seventh Lord Newborough at Rûg, 10 May 1995.

84. Sale particulars, see n. 56 above.

85. P. Brooks, *Have you Heard about Blakeney?* (North Walsham), 1985, 2.

86. G. Jenkins, *Traditional Country Craftsmen* (London, 1965), 102.

87. B. Greenhill, *The Merchant Schooners* (3rd edn., London, 1988), 75.

88. Newman & Field were Birmingham-based suppliers of a wide range of maritime, catering and domestic metal equipment, who regularly published an illustrated catalogue. This and other similar catalogues in the Merseyside Maritime Museum's collections have been invaluable in identifying items in the Wynn Collection.

89. T. K. Derry and T. I. Williams, *A Short History of Technology* (Oxford, 1960), 516–17, 695–8.

90. K. Sutton-Jones, *Pharos, the Lighthouse Yesterday, Today and Tomorrow* (Salisbury, 1985), 120–5.

91. W. Robinson, lamp-maker, worked at 33 Mill Street, Toxteth, but not at Canning Dock, according to *Gore's Liverpool Directories*.

92. GRO XD2/13440.

93. Wynn, *Short History*.

94. R. G. W. Anderson, J. Bennett and B. Gee, *A Handlist of Scientific Instrument Makers' 'Trade Catalogues'* (Edinburgh, 1990), 82–8.

95. Ibid., 38.

96. GRO XD2/13456, log book of the steam yacht *Mira*, 1891–3, 1895 and 1896.

97. GRO XD2/13380, inventories of the *Arvon* and *Sapphire*, 1825–31.

98. GRO XD2/4111, Frederick Wynn's diary, 1874–8.

99. Wynn, *Short History*.

100. G. Jenkins, *Nets and Coracles* (Newton Abbot, 1974), 301.

101. A. S. Davidson, *Samuel Walters – Marine Artist Fifty Years of Sea, Sail and Steam* (Coventry, 1992), 5 and 125.

102. GRO, Beaumaris Register of Shipping, 11/1795, two-masted schooner with one deck, 34 feet (10.4 m) long, 10 feet (3 m) beam, 5 feet (1.5 m) depth of hold, 17 tons, built at Caernarfon in 1795, sold and re-registered at Liverpool in 1804.

103. J. Cusack, 'The Rise of Yachting in England and South Devon, 1640–1827', in S. Fisher (ed.), *Recreation and the Sea* (Exeter, 1997), 101–41.

104. GRO XD2/13380, the names are found in a bundle of thirty-eight items of accounts for repairs and sundries, 1825–31.

105. A. Eames, *Ships and Seamen of Anglesey* (Llangefni, 1971), 422–4.

106. Letter to author, 13 April 1989: 'This was a wooden plate very nicely carved under the transom and was fitted on the inside of the transom. I was very upset to find when I came to look for it, which was one time a place of safe-keeping, that it was missing'.

107. John Brockbank's Day Book, September 1789,
     Mr. Sandys boat Graithwate Boat

Lth. Keel	17
Lth aloft	19 . . . 6
Bth moulded	6 . . . 4
Depth	2 . . . 4

best English oak as little Joiner work as possible made for 4 oars . . . a steady rowing boat.
Bth stern 3 . . . 5 depth 2 . . . 0 Tuck 1 . . . 5
One one cost £12 . . . 18 is 17 years old.

Estimate for new boat £17. 14*s*. 0*d*. including painting.

108. See n. 106.

109. GRO Beaumaris Register of Shipping, 20/1828.

110. GRO XD2/13380.

111. GRO Beaumaris Register of Shipping, 132/1826. The *Arvon* measured 29 feet 6 inches (9 m) in length and 10 feet (3 m) breadth, was clinker built with a shallop (i.e. schooner) rig, and had been built at Caernarfon by Richard Samuel in 1826. It is not clear why the Hon. Charles Irby disposed of her so quickly to Thomas John Wynn.

112. GRO XD2/13379, log book of the *Arvon*, 1825–7.

113. GRO XD2/9076, miscellaneous accounts for October 1836.

114. GRO XD2/13379, log book of the *Sapphire*, 1828–30.

115. GRO XD2/13382–13393, accounts for the *Sapphire*, 1828–9, including the crew's wages.

116. GRO Beaumaris Register of Shipping, 20/1828.

117. GRO XD2/13380, inventory of the *Sapphire*.

118. Letter to author from Michael Wynn, 13 April 1989.

119. Quoted in N. Wigglesworth, *Victorian and Edwardian Boating from Old Photographs* (London, 1987), caption to plate 32.

120. GRO XD2/13380, inventory of the *Sapphire*.

121. J. Kearon, 'The Ladies' gig', *Classic Boat* (May 1992), 41.

122. GRO XD2/58.312, William Roberts, Chester, correspondence with Frederick Wynn, 1900.

123. O. Roberts, 'Ladies' gig or lady's gig', *Maritime Wales*, 19 (1997–8), 90–2. Eames, *Ships and Seamen*, 424 for the Beaumaris reference and for Aberdovey, L. Lloyd, *A Real Little Seaport: The Port of Aberdyfi and its People 1565–1920*, vol. 2 (Caernarfon), 1996, 244–5 and GRO XD2/9164, subscription to the Dinorwic Regatta, miscellaneous bills for August 1846.

124. Lloyd, *Real Little Seaport*, 171.

125. Roberts, 'Ladies' gig', 92.

126. *Chester Chronicle* (6 January 1934).

127. GRO XD2/9081, bills for her delivery, 1837.

128. Eames, *Ships and Seamen*, 426.

129. *Caernarvon and Denbigh Herald* (7 September 1850).

130. H. P. Spratt, *Science Museum, Handbook of the Collections Illustrating Marine Engineering – Descriptive Catalogue* (London, 1953), 25–6.

131. GRO XD/1668, 9 September 1846, John Napier to Thomas Assheton-Smith.

132. GRO, *Caernarvon Register of Shipping*, 25/1848.

133. W. J. Lowe, *British Steam Locomotive Builders* (Cambridge, 1975), 461–2.

134. D. R. MacGregor, *Merchant Sailing Ships 1815–1850* (London, 1984), 153.

135. J. Grantham, *Iron as a Material for Ship-Building* (London, 1842).

136. GRO XD2/13396, John Grantham, Liverpool, to Spencer Wynn, 30 September 1847. Grantham's correspondence runs from 13396 to 13496, 1847–9.

137. GRO XD2/13398.

138. GRO XD2/13400–13401, 13405.

139. GRO XD2/13411.

140. GRO XD2/13415.

141. GRO XD2/13417.

142. GRO XD2/13419.

143. GRO XD2/13421–13422.

144. GRO XD2/13423, Bennet Woodcroft (1803–1879) was an inventor who patented a form of screw propeller in 1832. This was extended in 1846 and covered later propeller designs in spite of the fact they were different from his original concept.

Thus he was able to claim a licence fee for the *Vesta*. He went on to patent a number of adjustable pitch propellers, the models of which are in the collection of the Science Museum, and to found the Patent Office Library. See J. Hewish, *The Indefatigable Mr Woodcroft: The Legacy of Invention* (London, 1979), 10–12.

145. GRO XD2/13431, 13435, 13436, 9194, there was correspondence about payments (13424, 13426 and 13428) between August and September 1848.

146. GRO XD2/13444, log book of the *Vesta*, 1852–8, 7 October 1852, 10.00 p.m., 'heavy sea washed away stern boat and all her gear'.

147. GRO XD2/13395, log book of the *Vesta*, 1848–51. Note that the first section is the log of the *Sapphire* for 1833.

148. J. Grantham, 'The *Vesta*', *Transactions of the Institute of Naval Architects*, 7 (1866), 55, 'Her boiler was much too small, but this has since been replaced, and she is now in excellent condition.'

149. L. Lloyd, *De Winton's of Caernarvon 1854–1892* (Caernarfon, 1994), 9, 18–19.

150. GRO XD/2 (additional plans) 1670 and 1673. There is also an undated plan of a 100 hp engine for *Vesta* which is in the same hand as 1670 and 1673, and therefore likely to have been drawn by de Winton.

151. GRO XD2/13444.

152. B. Greenhill and A. Gifford, *The British Assault on Finland, 1854–1855: A Forgotten Naval War* (London, 1988), 257.

153. *Liverpool Register of Shipping*, 41/1874.

154. Lloyd, *De Winton's*, plate 6.

155. GRO XD2/1673, linked with J. P. de Winton, 22 June 1852.

156. A. S. Davidson, *Marine Art and Liverpool Painters, Places and Flag Codes, 1760–1960* (Wolverhampton, 1986), 60–2, 67.

157. GRO XD2/13450–13451.

158. Dixon Kemp, *Yacht and Boat Sailing*, (4th edn. 1884), quoted in R. Crabtree, *The Luxury Yacht from Steam to Diesel* (Newton Abbot, 1973), 110–11.

159. GRO XD2/13456, log book of the *Mira*, 1891–3, 1895 and 1896.

160. Ibid., letter to author.

161. Jenkins, *Nets and Coracles*, 176–183.

162. I. Smart, 'Dartmouth – the Hardness Shipyards from Zion Slip to King's Quay', *Maritime South West*, 10 (1997), 99–136.

163. Information from the Simpson Strickland records kindly supplied by Dr Janet Cusack. She also noted that they contain a reference to a 30 foot launch called *Myosotis*, supplied to Frederick Wynn in 1899. This was probably a change of name.

164. Letter to author.

165. The Science Museum Collection contains a similar engine and boiler, see Spratt, *Science Museum*, 46 and 82.

166. Cusack, 'Rise of Yachting'.

167. GRO XD2/13471 (D/WYN/2/4), bundle (six items) of correspondence, specification, quotation and modifications, Simpson, Strickland & Co., Ltd., to Frederick Wynn, 1900–10.

168. GRO XD2/13472 (D/WYN/2/6/9–10), bundle (fourteen items) of correspondence, agreements and specifications, William White & Sons, East Cowes, to Frederick Wynn, 1901–2.

169. GRO XD2/13487, plan and specification for a 40 foot steam launch, Simpson, Strickland & Co., Ltd., to Frederick Wynn, 18 July 1906.

170. GRO XD2/13495–13496 (D/WYN/2/11), correspondence, specification and plan from Simpson, Strickland & Co., Ltd., and quotation from Kiwi Works, Caernarfon, to Frederick Wynn, 1909.

171. GRO XD2/13511, letter from Simpson, Strickland & Co., Ltd., to Frederick Wynn, 29 November 1915.
172. GRO XD2/58.312.
173. William Roberts's obituary, *Chester Observer* (5 January 1934).
174. GRO XD2/58.312, E. Timmins to Frederick Wynn.
175. D/WYN/1/4 the Certificate of Registration No. 118.509 was issued at Caernarfon on 20 September 1933.
176. GRO 13456 (D/WYN/2/20), log of the *Firefly II*, 1934.
177. The account of the *Firefly's* wartime career was compiled by Clive Brookes from records held by the Naval Historical Branch: Admiralty Red List, 25 February 1940–15 October 1944 (weekly), Special (Secret) Military Branch Acquaints (SMBA), 2231/8, 2255/6, 2271/13, 2495/26, 2560/15, 2576/10, 2591/20, 2593/19, Small Craft Service List, Adm. 199/2429 and Adm. 199/2430, Warship Record Cards and Dockyard Ledgers held by Naval Historical Branch.
178. GRO XD2/13473–13474, letters and specification from G. L. Watson and others to Frederick Wynn, 1901–04.
179. GRO XD2/13491, disbursement book for *Mora*, 1906–14.
180. GRO XD2/13489, G. L. Watson & Co., bundle (four items) of correspondence and draft agreement to Frederick Wynn, 1906.
181. GRXD/13512, Pasley *v* Wynn.
182. In 1902, for example, he was afloat no less than twenty days between 22 January and 15 February, in his punt at Belan – see A. G. Credland, 'Sir Ralph Payne-Gallwey at Fort Belan', *Journal of the Arms and Armour Society*, 15/5 (March 1997), 290–306. This also gives a long description of the ballista. Payne-Gallwey published the results of this and other pieces of experimental archaeology in *Projectile-Throwing Engines of the Ancients* (London, 1907).

Index